PESTICIDES
&Health

Myths vs. Realities

A Position Paper of the

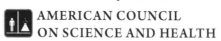

AMERICAN COUNCIL
ON SCIENCE AND HEALTH

Professor Allan S. Felsot
Washington State University

American Council on Science and Health
1995 Broadway, Second Floor
New York, New York 10023-5860
Tel. (212) 362-7044 • Fax (212) 362-4919
URL: http://www.acsh.org • Email: acsh@acsh.org

Publisher Name: American Council on Science and Health
Title: Pesticides and Health: Myths vs. Realities
Price: $10.95
Author: Allan S. Felsot
Subject (general): Science and Health
Publication Year: 2011
Binding Type (i.e. perfect (soft) or hardcover): Perfect

ISBN: 978-0-615-48512-6

Acknowledgements

The American Council on Science and Health (ACSH) appreciates the contributions of the reviewers named below:

John Berlau
Competitive Enterprise Institute

Christine Bruhn, Ph.D.
University of California, Davis

Janice E. Chambers, Ph.D., D.A.B.T., A.T.S.
Mississippi State University

Jay Lehr, Ph.D.
The Heartland Institute

Bob Krieger, Ph.D.
University of California, Riverside

Manfred Kroger, Ph.D.
The Pennsylvania State University

Angela Logomasini, Ph.D.
Competitive Enterprise Institute

Alan McHughen, D.Phil.
University of California, Riverside

Table of Contents

Executive Summary

Will we avert a crisis of food supply shortage? This question continues to loom large although population growth rate has tempered considerably, compared to projections 30 years ago. But several years ago, as food prices seemed to be on the verge of skyrocketing, owing to rapid increases in grain prices, we arguably got a taste of the future. When you consider uncertainty about climate variability and land use changes as well, we seem always on a precipice of doing with less rather than more. Fortunately, agricultural technology has thus far kept pace with a growing population. A crucial component of this toolbox has historically been a dynamic chemical technology, led by the availability of synthetic fertilizers and innovations in chemical pest control. This report analyzes the myths surrounding pesticide science and corrects each with a realistic perspective of the technology: how it is possible to kill pests without harming other organisms, how the science is regulated with a precautionary perspective, and, finally, with an analysis of claims made about hazards and the probability that these pose credible risks to health. This report makes the case for the benefits of pesticides, ranging from the protection of crop yields to the protection of public health. Indeed, the benefits are abundant enough that one can simply state that the availability of pesticides has significantly improved human health.

Controversy surrounding pesticide use at first glance would seem to date back to the 1962 publication of Rachel Carson's *Silent Spring*. However, this superficial analysis ignores the long history of pesticide control statutes such as the Federal Food, Drug, and Cosmetic Act (FFDCA 1938) and the Federal Insecticide, Fungicide, Rodenticide Act (FIFRA 1947). One might argue about the effectiveness of these laws, but they have been amended many times, before and after *Silent Spring,* to address their weaknesses. Indeed, perhaps the most far-reaching modification was the Food Quality Protection Act of 1996 which, for the first time, oriented the main law, FIFRA, to consider risk to consumer health as the only basis for re-registering older chemicals and registering new products. Veneration of *Silent Spring* by advocacy groups has overlooked the reams of data already in the public sector that Carson had been reading to inform her literary endeavor.

And so, current pesticide laws have evolved and are arguably the most precautionary of all congressional mandates involving technology. Indeed, we assert that modern pesticide laws epitomize in action an otherwise vacuous precautionary principle that eschews risk assessment as a basis for risk management. Risk assessment rightfully recognizes the too often ignored principles that all chemicals (whether plant-derived or cooked up by humans) are subject to the same physical laws of thermodynamics and the principles of kinetics. Such recognition explains how we humans can eat a myriad mixture of plant chemicals, many of which are recognized as toxins themselves, arising from an evolution of plant metabolism that aids their survival against voracious predators and the vagaries of weather.

In this background of survival, the principle of "reasonable certainty of no harm" guides decisions about releasing man-made pesticides to help in the battle to protect crop yields and food quality. Economic analyses prove how food supply would become precarious without the use of chemical technology. Epidemiological analyses prove how eliminating an effective surface-sprayed insecticide like DDT has fostered large outbreaks of malaria, the mosquito-borne scourge of 300 million humans a year. Yet despite the proven benefits of pesticides, years of research have shown that these valuable tools cannot be used without proper management, and that, moreover, they should exhibit selectivity of pests over nontarget organisms so that they become complementary to natural biological control processes existing within all agricultural ecosystems.

Industry has responded to the goals and needs of a compatible pesticide technology with development of ever more selectively toxic chemicals that are used at comparatively low rates compared to the chemicals they are replacing in the marketplace. The recent generations of EPA-designated reduced-risk pesticides are in many cases tens to hundreds of times less toxic to fish, birds, and nontarget predators and parasitoids than chemicals that were introduced to farmers between the 1950s and 1970s. However, the biochemical theory of ligand-receptor and enzyme-substrate kinetics, in combination with considerations of pharmacokinetics, is applied herein to show that some of the older chemicals actually present little risk of adverse effects in association with realistic environmental rates of use.

Following explications of toxicological mechanisms of selectivity and the importance of considering pharmacokinetic factors influencing pesticide disposition within the body, this report specifically examines the claims about four types of contemporary pesticides—atrazine, chlorpyrifos, pyrethroids, and glyphosate. In each case study, the published scholarly literature is used to show that the perception of adverse effects has arisen as a result of mistaking—either through ignorance or ideology—laboratory studies of toxicological mechanisms for analysis of risk based on consideration of how the chemicals are actually used.

One important point to consider in any analysis of pesticide technology is the evolution of a dynamic system of management. That is, any reports of adverse effects are dealt with by development and implementation of new testing requirements or by changes in permissible uses of a product. The system provides feedback to both regulatory agencies and manufacturers themselves. The latter have historically responded by a focus on discovery of new products that meet the goals of a safer chemical technology. Unfortunately, public attitudes—fed by attention-seeking media scare stories— seem focused on the past and fail to see a comparatively rapid change in chemical technology and how it has been deployed. Similarly, public attention is drawn to misinterpretations and half-analysis of stories of hazards. However, scrutiny of the published literature has failed to find evidence of a credible probability of adverse human health effects derived from the use of modern pesticides as occurs in the real world, not in the laboratory-generated environment. Despite the headlines of hazard, modern chemical technology provides hope for continued improvement of human health, whether helping to make vegetables and fruits of high quality more abundant and cheaper, or to preserve (or indeed, enhance) the health of individuals and society at large.

A Rationale for Confronting Myths about Pesticide Technology

Over the last decade, food preference surveys as well as sales statistics show an increasing percentage of consumer preference for buying "organic," raw, and processed food products (Saba and Messina 2003; Hughner et al. 2007). Although the absolute numbers of individuals purchasing these food items compared to conventional items is still quite small (Hughner et al. 2007), the data seem to validate the perception that consumers generally have a negative opinion of pesticide use (Chipman et al. 1995; Makatouni 2002; Magnusson et al. 2003; Yiridoe et al. 2005). This negative opinion is related to several concerns, ranging from worry about the health effects of pesticide residue exposure to a mistrust of industries synthesizing and marketing pesticides (Chipman et al. 1995; Slovic 1999). Various surveys also suggest that consumers do not perceive any benefits from the use of pesticide technology (Hansen et al. 2003). Consumers may understand the need to manage crop and livestock pests, but they may also think that pesticides are not necessary to achieve this goal, or, alternatively, that they are overused in agriculture (Chipman et al.

5

1995). Risk perception surveys generally agree that consumers view pesticides as a high hazard technology that is uncontrollable, unknowable, and of little benefit to themselves (Chipman et al. 1995; Slovic 1987).

Given that pesticide technology encompasses a vast array of individual chemicals and formulated products, changing consumer perceptions seems to present an insurmountable obstacle in communicating risk. While consumers are reacting by expressing their feelings about a generic technology, the scientific expert is most likely focusing on the idiosyncrasies of an individual compound. Nevertheless, general principles of biochemistry and physiology are important for assessing pesticide technology. Application of these principles is crucial to properly regulating as well as using the technology. Furthermore, the benefits of the technology must be considered in light of the possible and likely adverse consequences of **not** using it.

The literature on the perception and communication of risk suggests that perhaps consumers are not the real audience in need of information about the intricacies of pesticide technology. For example, 84% of surveyed residents in Washington State did not think pesticide use and control was an environmental problem (LaFlamme and VanDerslice 2004). It seems that information may be better directed to legislative members and their staff (Cohen 1997). When these cohorts were surveyed, the most desired information was explanations of how risk assessments are conducted, with application to particular chemicals as an example. If legislators and their staffs are receptive to a better understanding of chemical technology through risk assessment, then dispelling misconceptions about pesticides as a precursor to rational risk management may not be an insurmountable task. After all, legislatures mandate regulation of the technology. Regulators themselves, therefore, must understand fundamental biochemical principles, as they regulate many kinds of chemicals.

Yet simply educating regulators may not be an effective way to dispel misconceptions. Comparisons of lay and expert opinion about chemical hazards in general revealed unpredictable disagreements about the hazard and risk of chemical technology among experts (for example, regulators and academic or industry researchers engaged in some aspect of toxicology) that were not too different from those expected between consumers and experts (Kraus et al. 1992; Mertz et al. 1998). If there is as wide a divergence of opinion among experts themselves as that which occurs between experts and consumers, one cannot expect to be very successful at risk communication unless some of these perceptions are addressed directly. Perhaps within the technical community itself insufficient attention has been paid to "common wisdom" in order to determine operational misconceptions about pesticide technology in general.

This report is a response to a need expressed for factual information among legislative authorities, but it also addresses experts themselves by considering tenuous the assumption of agreement about the risks of chemical technologies. Our analysis substitutes factual information (some fundamental principles of toxicology based on biochemical concepts, an overview of properties of modern "reduced risk" pesticides, and a delineation of pesticide benefits to human wellbeing) for misconceptions specifically about pesticide technology.

To communicate the fundamental principles of toxicology necessary for appropriately regulating pesticide technology, this report will first state misconceptions or myths about pesticides that can be gleaned from a combination of risk perception literature, as well as examining pesticide stories in the media (Felsot 2010). After stating a myth, the reality based on biochemical principles will be explained. Similarly, misconceptions related to the real benefits of pesticide use will be answered with examples of how pesticides actually contribute to protection of human health and a general improvement in wellbeing. Finally, to illustrate how misunderstandings of the nature of toxicology and epidemiology studies contribute to a skewed conflation of hazard and risk, the report will review some commonly used biodegradable pesticides and attempt to alleviate issues of specific concern. By discussing misconceptions and realities about pesticide technology, and highlighting particular pesticides, this report can provide risk communicators within the business community and government with a stronger technical basis for discussing pesticide issues.

One caveat needs emphasis up front. Arguments promoting global benefits from pesticide technologies as they've evolved over the past 40 years are not arguments against ensuring that these compounds have little risk as they are used. Rather, our regulatory system for pesticides has actually been quite precautionary. Ironically, as calls for adoption of a "precautionary principle" in place of a risk assessment process have begun to permeate governmental regulatory activity, pesticides are arguably the one technology where so-called tenets of this principle are actively practiced. Thus, another objective of this report is to clarify multiple aspects of pesticide technology that must be known if we wish to move past the myth that we have not properly considered hazards in the midst of overwhelming benefits.

Pesticides with Benefits for All: An Agricultural Perspective

Myth: Farmers use pesticides for their own economic gain without regard for need or a social responsibility to protect the environment. Pesticides are not needed for farming, as has been proven by the increasing adoption of organic farming.

Agricultural Reality: The Economic Perspective

Pesticide and fertilizer use has been recorded since ancient times, suggesting that ecosystem management is not a recent cultural attribute. In the context of modern agriculture, the objectives of pesticide use are to increase production efficiency and yields; reduce the cost of food and, especially, to increase the availability of grains, fruits, and vegetables; improve food quality and losses during transport and storage; improve soil conservation; and ensure a stable and predictable food supply (*NRC 2000*).

Pesticide use is widespread on farms, but more importantly, different classes of pesticides are differentially used (*NRC 2000; Padgitt et al. 2000*), suggesting that growers make decisions based on need rather than solely on prophylaxis. For example, in the U.S. during 2002 approximately 303 million acres of crops were harvested, and 95% were treated with some type of pesticide. However, 64% of the acreage was treated to control weeds (i.e., herbicide use), 22% to control insects (insecticide use), 6% to control diseases and nematodes (fungicide and nematicide use). Another 4% of the crop acreage was treated with a plant growth regulator for fruit thinning, growth control, or defoliation (Felsot and Racke 2007).

The proportional use of different kinds of pesticides (i.e., herbicides, insecticides, fungicides, etc.) shows that farmers do not monolithically use the chemicals on every acre. Rather, the data show that use is tied to specific need. Furthermore, the intensity of specific pesticide classes also varies significantly by crop. Grains tend to be disproportionately treated with herbicides, but fruit and vegetables mostly receive insecticide and fungicide applications (Table I). Farmers use the technology that controls the pest at hand — but, importantly, use is driven by need as influenced by weather conditions, anticipated and actual pest infestations, and the balancing of costs and returns.

The benefits of crop protection chemicals for improving and protecting crop productivity is difficult to separate from the effects of hybrid seed technology and other plant breeding advances. Nevertheless, an examination of crop yields relative to land under production shows that both types of technologies have had major contributions. For example, the greatest proportion of U.S. farmland is devoted to corn production. A historical examination of area of land, yields, and the introduction of different technologies over time suggests that insect control (mainly of the corn rootworm complex) has greatly enhanced the effectiveness of hybrid seed technology (Figure 1). Furthermore, the introduction of modern synthetic herbicides facilitated widespread adoption of conservation tillage in the Corn Belt, which in turn greatly reduced the major cause of environmental degradation in North America—soil erosion and sedimentation in rivers (Pimentel et al. 1995).

Table 1. Percentage Use of Pesticide Classes on Major Crops During Crop Years 2003 or 2004

Crop	Herbicide	Insecticide	Fungicide
Corn	95	29	<1
Soybean	97	4	1
Wheat	45	7	2
Cotton	98	64	7
Potato	91	84	91
Apple	42	94	90

USDA NASS 2004, 2005

Figure 1. U.S. Corn Production

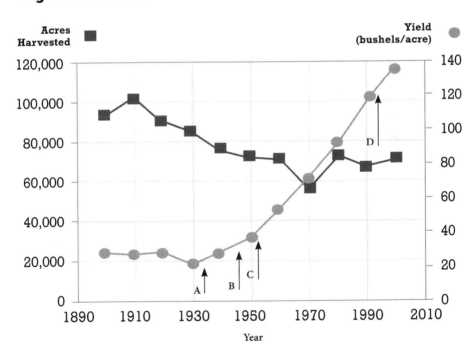

Historical trend in U.S. corn production and approximate timeline for introduction of crop production technologies. A: hybrid seeds; B: mineralized fertilizers; C: soil insecticides; D. transgenic crops (Carpenter et al. 2002).

Perhaps an even more compelling case for the role of crop protection chemicals, especially fungicides and fumigants, in crop production efficiency is suggested by potato production statistics. In 1900, nearly 3 million acres of potatoes were harvested, yielding an average of 52 cwt/acre (USDA 2005). In 1950, average yields were 153 cwt/acre. In crop year 2004, 1.2 million acres of harvested potatoes yielded an average 752 cwt/acre. Surely, advances in plant breeding play an important role in production increases, but by the 1950s, fumigants for control of nematodes became widely available — nearly coincidentally with the widespread adoption of mineralized fertilizers. But the production trends strongly suggest an environmental benefit because presently seven times more potatoes are produced per acre than were produced in 1900. If one thus extrapolates for other crops that yields have increased owing to adoption of modern technologies like improved breeding using biotechnology and chemical pesticides, then a large benefit is a return of farm land to other uses, such as forests and/or prairies and conservation of natural areas, as well as residences for a burgeoning population.

What is more, the aggregate economic benefits associated with pesticide use have been subjected to various empirical modeling exercises and expressed as the loss of production if pesticides were not used (NRC 2000). Production losses during the mid-1980s were estimated to be as high as 37% of total output (Pimentel et al. 1992). This estimated loss occurred despite pesticide use, but the estimate seems rather high when assessed against specific crop analyses. For example, one of the most destructive pests of potatoes, late blight disease, broke out in the Columbia Basin of Washington State and Oregon during 1995. Fungicide use rose from typically two applications per season to as many as 12 (Johnson et al. 1997). However, yield differences between the pre- and post-blight outbreak were only 4-6 percent. On the other hand, without any management, the blight epidemic could have reduced yields 30-100 percent.

Other economic analyses have projected the effect on fresh and processed vegetable and fruit yields if pesticide use were reduced 50 percent or simply not used at all (Knutson et al. 1993). Reductions in fresh fruit yields were 40 percent and 75 percent, respectively. Substantial reductions were projected in grain production under conditions of no herbicide use (Fernandez-Cornejo et al. 1998). Another study estimated that a total pesticide use ban would require an additional 2.5 million acres of vegetable and fruit production to make up for the yield loss (Taylor 1995). Although modeling estimates of the impacts of decreased pesticide use or no use seem large, the actual decrease in yields (and consequent effects on consumer prices) would depend on the availability of other alternative crop protection technologies or practices (NRC 2000). For example, field crops like corn can be grown with minimal herbicide use if tillage is used more frequently. Additionally, hand weeding, as is often practiced in certified organic crop production, along with tillage, can substitute for herbicide use. However, aggregate analysis of grain, vegetable, and fruit crop management, assuming only hand weeding and tillage without herbicide use, showed an average yield reduction of 20 percent (Gianessi and Reigner 2007). Furthermore, substitution of increased tillage for weed control would counter the benefits of reduced tillage for soil conservation.

Vegetable and fruit production would likely be the most adversely affected by wholesale loss of use of insecticides and fungicides, owing to their disproportional problems with insect pests and plant pathogens. Loss of pesticide availability would also adversely affect consumer prices, and potentially mean a loss of domestic sources of supply as production is relocated to other regions (Zilberman et al. 1991).

It's important to realize that the economic return-cost ratio for pesticide use is generally favorable. The ratio depends on the specific crop because the annual commodity price must be factored in, as well as the site-specific yield and expenses due to chemical purchases. Nevertheless, older estimates for return ranged from $4-$29 for every $1 spent (Metcalf and Luckman 1975), and more recent estimates suggest a $3-$6 rate of return per $1 spent (Zilberman et al. 1991; Pimentel et al. 1992). Significant for the grower is the comparatively low incremental cost of pesticide use relative to all production expenses. The most recent estimate (crop year 2002) is that purchase of pesticides represents 4.4% of total expenses, compared to the 12.7% of expenses for hired and contract farm labor (USDA 2004). Pesticides themselves help lower costs by substituting for labor. For example, fruit thinning required in the pome fruit industry is mostly done by chemical thinners but still requires some hand thinning if loads are deemed excessive.

Perhaps the most popular misconception among consumers of organic foods is that such products lack pesticide residues and other additives. The basis for this belief is the often-repeated argument that organic agriculture distinguishes itself from conventional production methods because no synthetic pesticides are used. Prolonged pronouncements of no synthetic pesticide use easily evolve into a consumer perception of no pesticide use. Contraction of no synthetic use to the equivalency of no use at all may be facilitated by the myth that somehow synthetic substances are generically different in their adherence to thermodynamic laws and reactivity than natural substances.

The reality is that U.S. rules for certification of organic production allow for the willful use of approved crop protection products. Under the Federal Insecticide, Fungicide, and Rodenticide Act (FIFRA) many of theses products are legally pesticides and must be registered with EPA (Felsot and Racke 2007). However, organic growers by rule cannot use synthetic materials unless approved by the National Organic Standards Board (NOSB). But no pesticide (NOSB-approved or otherwise) can be used in any type of farming practice unless vetted by EPA first. EPA does a comprehensive risk assessment on all chemicals submitted for registration, using the raw data submitted by a prospective pesticide registrant. Similarly, NOSB contracts with the Organic Materials Research Institute (OMRI) to do a comprehensive hazard assessment of materials proposed for certified organic production. In that case, similar questions are asked, except that the OMRI speculates whether a candidate product is really needed and therefore a credible substitute. One criterion would be that it is "less hazardous." Although a perspective of hazard differs from one that uses hazard along with exposure to characterize risk, some of the active ingredients used by nonorganic growers are the same as those used by certified organic growers. For example, spinosad insecticide, a complex macrocyclic lactone saccharide derived from a bacterial fermentation culture, is used by today's cherry growers regardless of their production philosophy. Even though NOSB policy tends to avoid substances that are toxic, spinosad has a biochemical mode of action that would classify it as a type of neurotoxin (Sparks et al. 2001; Orr et al. 2009).

The "purity" of organic food is further dispelled by analytical surveys of organic commodities to reveal that some contain synthetic pesticide residues both banned and currently registered, albeit much less frequently than so-called conventional foods (Baker et al. 2002). Residues in organic commodities are likely inadvertent, due to airborne transport and deposition, as well as soil residues from past use. Recognizing the ubiquity and mobility of environmental residues, NOP rules allow inadvertent pesticide residues up to 5 percent of the established federal tolerance level without a loss of organic certification. Whether one likes or dislikes pesticide use, past practices influence residues in food. However, current residue studies indicate that the vast majority of conventional foods have **no detectable pesticide residues** (FDA 2009; USDA AMS 2009).

In summary, various economic analyses are in agreement that pesticide use has been definitely associated with profitable returns to farmers (and thus to society), and it is not true that pesticides are used on every crop indiscriminately. The reality is that some crops require disproportionately more herbicide use and some crops require more insecticide and/or fungicide use. Thus, efforts to globally limit pesticide use fail to take into account specific and local needs for crop protection. Furthermore, certified organic producers have an array of pesticides they can use under the rules of the NOSB. Past land practices have led to detections of pesticide residues in organic food, but current analytical surveys show that so-called conventionally produced food most often has no detectable pesticide residues.

Agricultural Reality: Practical & Environmental Advantages of Crop Protection Chemicals

In addition to their economic benefits accruing from the objectives for which they are used, pesticides have certain advantages over other practices for crop protection (as well as production) that make them very convenient, efficient, and cost-effective (Metcalf and Luckman 1975). First, for most cropping systems, pesticides are the only practical available technology because other technologies are not available, unproved, or do not work efficiently. For instance, hybrids of certain crops may lack a pest-resistant cultivar. In other cases, a nonchemical pest control practice fails to work over time. An example of the latter situation is the apparent adaptation of western corn rootworms to the practice of annual corn-soybean rotations that were very successful in reducing the need for soil insecticides (Sammons et al. 1997; Rondon and Gray 2004).

Second, pesticides have rapid curative action in preventing loss of crop yield or protecting human and animal health. Thus, they can be used when a pest population becomes intolerable. One of the tenets of integrated pest management (IPM) is eschewing prophylactic sprays in favor of "as needed" treatments. Thus, there may be a very short window of time during which the pest needs to be controlled, and nonchemical methods may lack a rapid enough action.

Third, the diversity of locations where crops are grown means different pest complexes thrive under a wide range of climatic conditions. Pesticides have a wide range of properties, uses, and methods of application that can cover many problems as they arise. The inorganic pesticides used during the first half of the 20th century and the first wave of synthesized pesticides after 1950 were generally broad spectrum but not necessarily adequate for all cropping systems (Stern et al. 1959). Over the last thirty years new chemistries have been introduced to narrow the spectrum of activity. Along with new formulations and application methods, modern pesticides can be better tailored to specific crops' pest problems. Similarly, insecticides introduced over the last 15 years are also much less toxic to the natural biocontrol organisms than the broad-spectrum synthetics introduced during the 1950s. Furthermore, modern pesticides rapidly degrade in the environment and do not bioaccumulate in lipid tissues as did the chlorinated hydrocarbon and cyclodiene pesticides that were heavily used prior to their ban in the early 1970s.

A fourth benefit stems from herbicide use in grain production throughout the Corn Belt. Before the advent of synthetic chemical herbicides like atrazine, erosion was severe on even gently sloping lands because farmers relied on the moldboard plow and further cultivation of the soil during crop growth to control weeds. Many environmental scientists agree that eutrophication and sedimentation of aquatic resources due to runoff and erosion from agricultural land is the most important cause of water quality impairment, not to mention being reponsible for transportation problems as rivers backfill with sediment. By the 1960s, a few herbicides were commercially available and allowed farmers to consider substituting chemical control of weeds for turning the soil over and thereby making it highly susceptible to the erosion caused by wind and spring rains on bare soil. No-till agriculture bloomed, especially in corn production, because farmers were able to rely on herbicides. Aggregate soil erosion from tilled soil in four Corn Belt states (Illinois, Indiana, Iowa, Nebraska) was estimated at 14.9 tons/acre/year but only 2.8 tons/acre/year from untilled grain fields (Gianessi and Reigner 2006).

Furthermore, by eliminating the need to till soil, herbicides also allow for the conservation of fuel. Over 111 million gallons of fuel may be saved by using herbicides instead of tillage in the aforementioned four Corn Belt States (Gianessi and Reigner 2006). Lowered emissions of greenhouse gases are also associated with a reduction in fuel use (Robertson et al. 2000).

In addition to fuel reductions, an increased yield for every dollar invested in agricultural production significantly reduces per acre increases in carbon emissions; this is by virtue of avoiding the land clearing otherwise necessary to maintain sufficient production for an increasing population (Burney et al. 2010). Thus, current analyses support the idea that pesticide technology also contributes to environmental quality by virtue of enhancing yield.

Two other recent analyses also support the conclusion that there are both direct and indirect benefits to pesticide technology. Although the direct benefits of suppression of pest density, and thus suppression of damage, are obvious, indirect benefits can also be considerable. Some examples of the latter include increased financial resources for a community, due to greater producer profits; increased consumer access to fresh fruits and vegetables; and an increase in lands available for wildlife conservation (Cooper and Dobson 2007). Direct control of human and livestock pests (as discussed in the following sections) create similar secondary benefits for economic productivity, public health, and longevity.

An analysis of historical and contemporary management of cotton pests provides another affirmation of the benefit of pesticide technology and also suggests indirect benefits beyond a specific crop (Naranjo and Ellsworth 2009). Cotton has historically been a crop requiring arguably the highest per acre intensity of pesticide use. Cotton pest management in Arizona has evolved into a highly strategic system that employs both natural biological control organisms (i.e., predators and parasitoids) but also relies on highly selective insecticides for controlling the most important pests, which include the pink bollworm and whiteflies. Pink bollworms have been managed by use of cotton cultivars bred to contain the highly selective bacterial toxin protein derived from the naturally occurring insect pathogen *Bacillus thuringiensis*. Deployment of such cultivars can conserve predator populations. The whitefly, on the other hand has, been successfully managed by judicious integration of highly selective insecticides that affect insect development. The availability of such insecticides has not only increased profits by reducing the overall need for pesticides, it has also indirectly benefited other regional crops attacked by whiteflies: These now show an overall reduction in their populations. Thus, innovative pesticide technology has resulted in "an unprecedented stability of ecosystem services and major economic and environmental gains in Arizona cotton that has extended to benefit the entire agroecosystem of the region" (Naranjo and Ellsworth 2009).

Pesticides with Benefits for All: A Public Health Perspective

Myth: Pesticides offer no benefit to public health and, arguably, detract from it.

The Public Health Reality: Historical and Modern

Daily life in the developed countries of the West is not likely plagued by insect-transmitted infectious diseases. While it is true that the yellow fever vector mosquito *Aedes aegypti* once haunted the streets of New Orleans, a program of publicly financed mosquito control arose in the 1960s and spread throughout the U.S. to dampen the disease-transmission potential of insects. Even so, over the last decade, West Nile virus, transmitted by the bite of the *Culex* mosquito, has spread from New York to California, becoming endemic in every state (Artsob et al. 2009). Lyme disease, a spriochete bacterium transmitted by the bite of the tiny deer tick, disables nearly 20,000 people each year (Bacon et al. 2008); it is in many places now in the U.S., although the epicenter is in New England. Insect bites are mostly a nuisance to citizens in highly developed countries, but the last decade of West Nile virus epide-miology shows the need for vigilance about infectious disease control even as megacities and exurbs pave over widening expanses of natural lands. Further-more, the widespread outbreak and spread of West Nile virus has had observ-ably negative impacts on bird populations (LaDeau et al. 2007).

Recent experience indicates the need for vigilance against arthropod-vectored diseases even in developed countries—but the situation is surely more dire on a continent like Africa, where publicly financed programs are in-frequent, and poor when they exist. *Anopheles* mosquitoes today still transmit per annum over 500 million cases of malaria (WHO 2010), a disease caused by *Plasmodium falciparum*, a protist requiring both the mosquito and human body in which to complete its life cycle. Malaria causes paroxysms of fever, often several times each day. With so many infected, economies become inef-ficient as workers are struck ill. And because infant and child nutrition is so deficient in these countries, a nearly unimaginable 800,000 children die from mosquito-transmitted malaria each year.

But many countries have malaria under control. They adopted the use of DDT, the chemical technology used by the military during WWII and by the European Command after the war to control mosquito populations. Data on malaria incidence before and after the advent of DDT proved that the pesticide could be effective without causing acute harm (Hayes 1991). The evidence for lack of acute harm became apparent when millions of Europeans were directly dusted to control lice that transmitted a form of typhus caused by the bacterium *Rickettsia*.

However, DDT was essentially banned in the U.S. in 1972 when the recently-created EPA decided to suspend its registration for any agricultural use. (In fact, the decision was entirely the work of EPA's first administrator, William Ruckelshaus.) Unfortunately, the history of agricultural use of DDT and its demise as an effective pest control technology on crops has been con-flated with its continued success with mosquito control in lesser developed countries of Africa, parts of Latin America, and parts of Asia. Although DDT was memorialized into infamy by Rachel Carson's *Silent Spring*, it was the ag-ricultural use of the chemical that got it into trouble, not the public health use.

Even so, since Carson's time, how DDT is used in public health has been the key to its successful control of mosquitoes where they matter, in the house. During and shortly after WWII, spraying of DDT was widespread in the environment. However, by the 1950s it was well known that mosquitoes rested on walls and ceilings of buildings. Thus, by the late 1950s researchers had already established the efficacy of a "space spray," wherein only resting areas on walls would be treated (Barlow and Hadaway 1956).

To this day, the public likely does not understand how DDT is actually used, and thus visions of *Silent Spring* dominate the conversation. So prevalent is the misunderstanding that a number of countries decided to eschew its use — with devastating consequences for malarial incidence. Re-adoption of the limited spraying of house walls was associated with a rapid decline in malarial incidence (Roberts et al. 1997). However, aerial spraying for mosquitoes is still viewed as effective under certain circumstances for some insect vectored diseases. The benefits of using adulticides to control West Nile virus mosquito vectors have been shown to substantially exceed costs as well as effectively protect human health without adverse health effects or ecological problems from pesticide exposure (Peterson et al. 2006; Davis et al. 2007; Carney et al. 2008; Barber et al. 2010).

Pertinently, public health protection specialists have long known that DDT alone is not enough to control the scourge of malaria-infested mosquitoes. Mosquito larval, egg-laying, and breeding habitat must be monitored and managed. Western countries now use insecticides based on microbial toxins, namely *Bacillus thuringiensis israeliensis (Bti)* and *Bacillus sphaericus*. *Bti* and *B. sphaericus* are incredibly specific, naturally occurring bacteria that are toxic only when ingested by mosquito larvae. These organisms are still deemed pesticides, specially regulated under EPA's biopesticides program (EPA 2010).

In addition to habitat management for mosquito control, individuals are encouraged to protect themselves with mosquito netting around their beds at night. Emphasis has been placed on using insecticide-impregnated bed netting, which can be effective when whole communities are included in control programs. However, even such relatively passive control measures are very much influenced by the type of insecticide deployed (e.g., irritant vs. non-irritant effects) (Curtis and Mnzava 2000), further illustrating that the benefits of pesticides depend on the appropriate use of specific chemicals.

One aspect of protecting public health that is not often mentioned is the potential of pesticides to reduce microbial contamination and the associated production of fungal toxins. Overlooked is the use of chlorine and other disinfectants, all of which are registered pesticides, in water treatment. U.S. consumers appreciate water devoid of bacterial contaminants and know implicitly that bacterial infection from drinking water is very rare here. However, inadequately treated public supplies do occur, as evidenced by the outbreak of cryptosporidium in a Wisconsin water supply during 1993 (MacKenzie et al. 1994). A water-borne outbreak of pathogenic *E. coli* in Walkerton, ON during 2000 was also definitively connected to inadequate chlorination (Hrudey et al. 2003).

Anti-pesticide activists may try to assert that pesticide use is all about blemish-free fruit and vegetables. True, use of crop protection technologies reduces marking and scarring, thereby filling to overflowing produce counters with picture-book food. But insect feeding causes harm that makes a food more susceptible to fungal invasion. Certain fungi commonly associated with crops produce mycotoxins that have well-documented physiological effects in mammals, including humans and livestock (Marasas 2001). Allowing insect or plant disease injury to progress without protecting a crop only increases the likelihood of mycotoxin residues. Indeed, the problem's gravity is evidenced by an international standard for maximum allowable residues of mycotoxins. Furthermore, the value of protecting crops against direct insect feeding has been proven with the adoption of corn genetically bred with a gene from *Bacillus thuringiensis* (called Bt corn) to produce a very insect-specific protein that kills the European corn borer. This insect damages corn and is arguably the major cause of fungal mycotoxin contamination, as damaged seed is pushed into storage. Mycotoxins are considered both human and livestock hazards with carcinogenic, neurotoxic, and teratogenic effects. However, Bt corn has substantially lower levels of mycotoxin contamination than corn not protected against corn borers (Bakan et al. 2002; Wu 2006). Thus Bt corn, which is regulated as a pesticide, helps keep grain quality within established regulatory standards that protect against mycotoxin exposure.

One practical benefit of pesticide use that is often overlooked is tied both to public health protection of workers as well as economics of production. Herbicides, which are used more frequently and in greater quantities than any other pesticide class, are quickly applied to all kinds of crops and thus eliminate the need for hand labor to hoe out weeds (Gianessi and Reigner 2007). Hand labor is expensive, and its availability is diminished by a shortage of people willing to become part of a migrant worker culture that moves from farm to farm. One application of herbicides for weed control in a single field is worth the hand labor of tens to hundreds of workers. The aggregate numbers are startling for just four major Belt States alone (i.e., Illinois, Indiana, Iowa, Nebraska). Economic analysis of labor requirements in the absence of herbicide use has estimated the need for a total of 338 million hours of work by over two million workers (Gianessi and Reigner 2006). Considering that less than 2% of the entire US population (approximately 6 million people) works on farms, replacing chemicals with people is not practical.

Perhaps just as important is to question how people would fare doing strenuous physical labor in the sun for a typical 8-hour work day. Sun exposure may explain elevated lip cancer risks, as well as the slightly elevated skin cancer risk, among farmers (Aquavella et al. 1998). Musculoskeletal health would likely be seriously impaired, given the physical nature of hand-pulling and hoeing weeds. As evidence of such physically adverse impacts, California instituted an administrative policy prohibiting the use of short-handled hoes. Organic lettuce growers rely on hand weeding to attain profitable production and have petitioned the State of California against stricter labor rules, ostensibly because sufficiently effective approved herbicides are unavailable (James 2005). Thus the lack of appropriate available pesticides adds to labor costs as it simultaneously raises the issue of hand-weeding labor's impact on worker health.

The foregoing story of public health benefits now comes full circle, back to the historical roots of using pesticides directly to affect insects afflicting our bodies. The flowers of chrysanthemums (specifically *Chysanthemum cinerariaefolium*) were used in the early 1800s by Southeastern Europeans and Persians to produce an extract called pyrethrum that alleviated a lice sufferer's scourge. Thus, over a span of less than 200 years, we have taken and improved upon Mother Nature's chemistry to improve our own public health. Which leads to the next myth about chemical pesticides.

Synthetic Chemistry for Crop Protection: Humans Imitate Plants and Bacteria

Myth: Synthetic chemical pesticides are unnatural and cannot be degraded. Thus, they are particularly dangerous in comparison with natural products derived from plants.

Technological Reality: We've Always Copied the Good Ideas of Plants and Bacteria

Many organisms, especially plants, produce chemicals incidental to their normal energy-producing biochemistry that function to ward off predators, protect seeds, or attract insects for pollination (Ames et al. 1990a, 1990b; Ames and Gold 1997). Sometimes, these chemicals are just by-products of metabolism that may serve other purposes, or they are perhaps excretory products that would be toxic if allowed to accumulate in the cells. Sometimes we can only speculate about the evolutionary role of these chemicals. For example, apples contain acetic acid. Although it's a natural component of apples, the acid is nevertheless listed as a hazardous substance, and the MSDS sheet lists horrific adverse effects from exposure, including vomiting, diarrhea, ulceration, bleeding from intestines and circulatory collapse. Perhaps the evolutionary benefit of such a metabolic pathway and storage in fruit accrued from the known antiseptic qualities of acetic acid (Levine 1940). Similarly, bacteria produce well-known toxins that ostensibly provide some protection against predaceous protists or other bacteria. A pertinent example of humans using such hazardous bacterial metabolites is the subcutaneous injection or topical epidermal application of the highly toxic botulinim neurotoxin, which is derived from the anaerobic food spoilage organism *Colstridium botulinin*; it is commonly used for cosmetic or corrective purposes (Collins and Nasir 2010).

The examples of acetic acid and botulinin, as well as other instances of natural toxins in food, are but some examples of the many incidental chemicals produced by plants and/or bacteria that are quite toxic in high doses. Certain fungi of the genus *Aspergillus* grow on cereals and produce chemicals called aflatoxins that are hundreds of times more potent than any synthetic pesticide synthesized by humans. Yet our perspective about the risks of pesticides does not apply to *Aspergillus*, as our concerns are focused on the timely application of a fungicide on stored grains—the right thing to do in order to protect food and avert health problems.

Because chemicals produced by plants are functional, evolution has arguably resulted in a form of chemical technology. Through our own chemical technology, aren't we just "imitating" our botanical and bacterial counterparts? For example, Swiss cheese results from bacterial species that produce substantial amounts of propionic acid when growing on milk products. The propionic acid is a by-product, along with the carbon dioxide formation that creates the familiar holes, but it also suppresses prolific fungal (i.e., mold) growth (Suomalainen and Mayra-Makinen 1999). Today, humans add synthesized propionates to baked goods to obtain the same protection.

Members of indigenous cultures have long used plants as their medicines. The knowledge of which plants to use, how to prepare them, and the amounts to administer has been passed from generation to generation. Isn't the use of flora for our benefit, our survival, a form of chemical technology? Perhaps we should consider generations of trial and error in discovering beneficial and harmful plants as analogous to a risk assessment process.

Humans have always used chemical technology. Whether the chemicals are made by plants, bacteria, or by our own hands is irrelevant. Some have maintained there is a difference between chemicals from the tropical rain forests and chemicals from the giant chemical industries. But principles of environmental chemistry would dictate that behavior of a chemical is governed primarily by thermodynamics, not how it was made.

Some would say that our coevolution with plants over many generations has allowed us to detoxify many of the natural dietary chemicals. Consider, however, that many of our foods are recent inventions of selective breeding that still possess the same potentially toxic chemicals as their wild ancestors.

In considering synthetic pesticides, a credible argument can be made for the human use of tools to synthesize other useful tools, e.g., pesticides, as an evolutionary adaptation. This adaptation is analogous to the evolution of secondary metabolic pathways in plants that result in biochemicals protective of their survival.

You've Come a Long Way, Baby

Myth: Pesticides used today are all just like DDT, and thus just as dangerous. All pesticides are alike and have not changed since DDT. All synthetic chemicals are equally hazardous.

The Reality of Modern Pesticide Technology: Dynamics & Evolution

The arguments set forth in this report by no means defend the properties of DDT as ideal. Rather, the aforementioned discussion focused on DDT's effectiveness in controlling resting adult mosquitoes when the compound is used in a very specific and locally confined manner inside of a dwelling. Furthermore, it is used not solely but as an adjunct to pyrethroid insecticide-impregnated mosquito netting. Ideally, government-funded programs of habitat management would accompany individuals' attempts at mosquito control.

All chemicals have distinct physicochemical properties that make them behave differently from each other. Chemicals with similar structural elements, i.e., arrangement of the same atoms, will behave similarly yet still possess idiosyncratic properties. Chemicals having divergent structural elements will be even more unlike one another. Thus, to conclude that all pesticides, because they can kill pests, are just like DDT is to seriously lack an understanding of basic chemistry, not to mention the complexity of biochemical interactions.

The specific physicochemical properties of DDT that made it unique were very low water solubility (it is practically insoluble in water) and resistance to extensive degradation in organisms or on plant surfaces. On the other hand, the very low water solubility of DDT and its one environmental oxidation product, DDE, drove it to move readily into the atmosphere. Such a mechanism, commonly called "phase partitioning" in the field of environmental chemistry, was arguably the most influential process in widespread environmental distribution of DDT. Unfortunately, its properties of persistence, along with broad-spectrum biological activity against pests and beneficial insects (e.g., predators and parasitoids feeding on the pests) alike made it a poor choice for use in agriculture after WWII. Add the rapid development of insects resistant to its effects, and the stage was set for entomologists—long before the publication of *Silent Spring*—to recommend that it not be used on field and orchard crops.

Evidence of the dynamic nature of industry's response to changing pest-control needs, and thus its ability to synthesize and test new chemical designs, is a new group of chemicals called organophosphorus (OP) insecticides that were introduced into commercial agriculture in the late 1960s. Soon thereafter, a second group, called methyl carbamate (CB) insecticides, was introduced. OP and CB insecticides had short persistence in the environment, and at least some were not quite as toxic to predators and parasitoids. At the very least, they gave growers more options for integrating chemical use with biological control (Stern et al. 1959).

As DDT and related compounds fell into disfavor in agriculture, and pressure from regulatory decisions mounted, growers became heavily reliant on OP and CB insecticides. Overreliance on one technology often leads to pest resistance, but again the dynamic nature of the technology shone: The British had started working on modifying the natural insecticidal components of pyrethrum extracts, i.e., the pyrethrins, to produce light-stable compounds, and thus longevity in the field beyond a few hours. Fortunately, such compounds were far less toxic than the OPs to mammals, which is always of concern for worker health, as well as for birds. Unfortunately, fish were quite susceptible to the new synthetic derivative of the natural pyrethrins — just as they were to the natural products. However, the amounts used dropped from two or more pounds applied per acre to ranges of 0.1-0.2 pounds per acre. Appropriate timing of application, combined with good soil management practices to protect against erosion, could resolve the likelihood of runoff into aquatic habitats in sufficient quantities for fish kills. Thus another chemical with a different mode of biochemical action was added to the grower's toolbox. Unfortunately, overreliance on a particular chemical again resulted in development of resistant insects.

By the time of pyrethroid development, insecticide manufacturers had begun to focus on the concept of biorational design of chemicals with insecticidal activity (Menn and Henrick 1981). This concept took two forms. First, natural products with biological activity could be tinkered with, altering their structure to more precisely target their activity. Development of synthetic pyrethroids were initially based on structures of the natural pyrethrins. By the late 1970s, new insect growth regulators were synthesized based on natural hormones or plant metabolites that exhibited either juvenile hormone agonistic or antagonistic activity (Menn and Henrick 1981). The latter endeavors were enhanced by basic research on specific biochemical and physiological systems of pests. The second form of biorational design was the combination of more traditional synthesis methods with the optimization of structure-activity relationships, which occasionally resulted in compounds that could affect specific physiological mechanisms of insect pests. For example, an array of compounds have been synthesized based on the model compound diflubenzuron, serendipitously found to inhibit the synthesis of chitin in the insect exoskeleton (Menn 1980). These types of compounds are still being used today, and more recent discoveries of their effective use as termiticides have won EPA Presidential Green Chemistry Awards. Many of these compounds with effects on specific insect physiological systems could be used at low rates per acre, owing to their potent effects on the pests — even better, their impacts on predators were low, because they have to be directly eaten for maximal biological effect.

The idea of a silver bullet, as exemplified by DDT's deployment and overuse in agriculture, had disappeared from the mindset of industrial research by the mid 1980s; this was because new discoveries of chemicals with completely different modes of action continued unabated. The new bevy of chemicals since the late 1980s eventually were recognized by EPA as meeting their criteria for "reduced risk" (EPA 1993). These chemicals were ultimately used at lower use rates than many other chemicals previously marketed, and they were even less toxic to mammals, birds, fish, and aquatic invertebrates (Table 2, Figures 2-5). With some exceptions, these chemicals tended to be more selective for killing pests rather than predators. Thus, even more opportunity

Table 2. Comparative mammalian toxicity of insecticides registered over the last decade and designated as 'reduced risk' by EPA.

Active Ingredient	Commercial Formulation	Oral LD50 (mg/kg)	Dermal LD50 (mg/kg)	NOAEL (mg/kg/d)
Azinphos-methyl	Guthion	4.4	155	0.149
Chlorpyrifos	Lorsban	223	222	0.03
Acetamiprid	Assail	1064	>2000	7.1
Indoxacarb	Advion	1277	>5000	2
Pyriproxyfen	Esteem	4253	>2000	35
Methoxyfenozide	Intrepid	>5000	>2000	10.2
Novaluron	Rimon	>5000	>2000	1.1
Pymetrozine	Fulfil	>5000	>2000	0.377
Spinosad	Success	>5000	>2000	2.7
Rynaxypyr	Altacor	>5000	>5000	158

To place the concept of reduced risk in perspective, parameters for azinphos-methyl and chlorpyrifos are shown because these were developed prior to EPA's initiative, stated in PR Notice 93-2 (EPA 1993).

arose for compatibly integrating these new chemistries into programs that would try to deploy ecologically-based, integrated pest management strategies.

The historical use of herbicides and the evolution of chemical classes parallel that of the insecticides — with a major exception. Prior to WWII, about the only herbicides available that could be practically used on fields were dinitrophenolic compounds like dinoseb and DNOC. These uncouplers of oxidative phosphorylation had a general mechanism of toxicity that made them nonselective for weeds, insects, and fungi. However, by the 1940s 2,4-D was discovered and found to mimic the natural plant hormone auxin (indole-3-acetic acid), ushering in the discovery of a very specific plant mechanism of toxic action. Thus, biological activity at field application rates was only applicable to plants and not animals. Surprisingly, 2,4-D was only toxic to certain dicotyledon (broadleaf) plants. Thus, 2,4-D could be applied to a bluegrass lawn or a field of wheat without damaging it. Interestingly, dichlorophenol, a putative metabolite of 2,4-D, is synthesized naturally by a soil fungus and its isomeric analog is used by some ticks as a sex pheromone, as well as an ant repellent by a grasshopper species (Gribble 1998). The discovery of the specific biological activity of 2,4-D reiterates an important concept in biochemistry alluded to before — selectivity. Thus, as manifested by the aforementioned evolution of insecticide chemistry, synthetic organic chemical herbicides invented circa WWII allowed for biological selectivity between animals and plants but also within the Plant Kingdom itself.

By the late 1950s, the most intensely used pesticide of all time, atrazine, was synthesized and discovered to have only one biochemical effect at field application rates—namely, inhibition of a particular electron acceptor in Photosystem II of plants. Atrazine's potency is selectively limited to broadleaf weeds but has no activity against grasses like corn. To curtail a long story, herbicide synthesis continued to produce compounds with other modes of action specific to plants and with zero potency at field application rates to any other types of organisms.

Perhaps the ultimate in the development of new chemistry with limited impact on anything but the targeted pest was Monsanto's synthesis and

Figure 2. Acute toxicity of new insecticides to fish (rainbow trout or close relative).

In this graph and subsequent ones, parameters for chlorpyrifos and azinphos-methyl are shown for comparison.

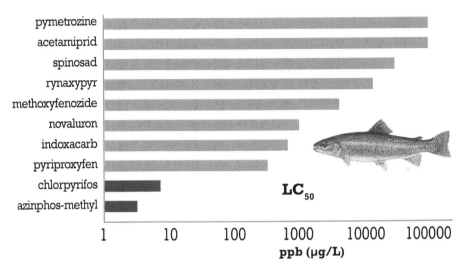

Figure 3. Acute toxicity of new insecticides to the aquatic invertebrate *Daphnia magna*.

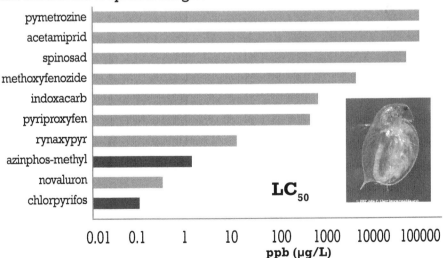

Figure 4. Acute toxicity of new insecticides to birds (quail).

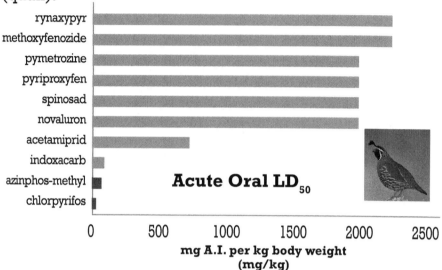

Figure 5. Application rates per acre of new insecticides.

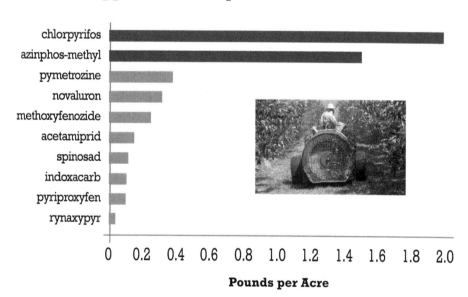

development of glyphosate herbicide. Considered by the European Union as well as EPA to be a reduced risk herbicide with no toxicological concerns at the designated legal rates of field application, glyphosate has become the most widely used herbicide in the agricultural sector, especially with the development of crops like soybean, corn, and cotton that can resist its phytotoxicity.

The history of pesticide synthesis as a dynamic process, with researchers adapting their skills in biology and chemistry to ever more selectively bioactive compounds, leads to another myth about pesticides. As will be explained, this next myth also reveals a serious misunderstanding of concepts like toxicity, hazard, and risk — as well as a lack of knowledge about basic biochemistry.

It's Still About the Dose (and Timing)

Myths: Exposure to pesticides results in adverse health effects. Hazards of pesticides are equivalent to the risk of adverse effects.

The Reality of A Modern Biochemical Perspective on Toxicity, Hazard, and Risk

Ultimately, consumers want to know whether any technology is "safe". The concept of chemical safety among regulatory toxicologists is understood not as a quantitative unitary concept but rather as a description of a probability of a reasonable certainty of no harm. The validity of the concept of reasonable certainty of no harm, which is actually more science policy than science, depends on a distinction among the terms "toxicity," "hazard," and "risk." Distinguishing these terms and, moreover, defining them from a biochemical perspective, is crucial for a rational argument about the nature of pesticide use in modern society.

Toxicity is an inherent property of both a particular molecule (called the substrate or ligand) and any organismal enzymes or receptors (tissue cell macromolecules) that it can react or interact with. Such interaction results in a physiological reaction that could be inimical to the survival of an organism, and thus the substrate or ligand would be called a toxicant. By definition, pesticides are inimical to the lives of pests, thus pesticides are toxicants. The concept of "inherent property" refers to the fact that the three-dimensional structure of any toxicant must be complementary to the three dimensional structure of an enzyme or receptor for any interaction to occur. In addition to structure, molecular interactions are also influenced by physicochemical properties related to molecular charges and hydrophobicity. Such interactions occur very readily if the structures of a toxicant and its receptor are highly complementary. In such cases, the substance is considered highly potent. Interactions would occur with structures not as complementary only under conditions of inordinately high toxicant concentrations, typically those not likely to be found in the environment but certainly possible to create in the lab when animals are tested. A toxicant requiring extremely high concentrations in order to have an interaction with an enzyme or receptor, and thus cause an adverse physiological reaction, would be considered to have low potency. In summary, then, toxicity is a property inherent to any molecule, allowing it to elicit an adverse physiological response when an organism has specific enzymes, receptors, or other macromolecules whose three-dimensional structures are complementary.

The nature of fundamental thermodynamic and kinetic laws governing chemical interactions prescribes that any molecule could, hypothetically, interact with any other molecule. However, the concentration of the two molecules must be sufficiently high for the interaction to have any reasonable probability of occurring. This latter concept leads to the definition of "hazard." Hazard describes the potential of a chemical to cause harm under a particular set of conditions. In other words, toxicants are not inherently hazardous unless the context is conducive to the sufficient interaction of the toxicant with the particular enzymes or receptors to which it is complementary. To study how chemicals interact with organisms, scientists in the laboratory always create conditions in which the subject chemical will be hazardous. Often the conditions are concentrations (or doses) of chemical sufficient to cause an observable response in a test population of organisms. If the conditions of the exposure change (for example, using a very low dose) then the hazard may change or simply disappear altogether.

Experiments repeatedly show that natural and synthetic substances at one dose may have no adverse effects on an organism, but at another higher dose can cause harm. This concept, frequently called "the dose makes the poison", is the fundamental principle guiding toxicological studies, and it is discussed in all basic toxicology textbooks. Of course, that popular toxicological aphorism belies more complex interactions between a substance and its effects on an organism. The dose required to cause deleterious effects within a population of organisms can vary depending on the route of exposure (oral, dermal, or inhalational), the length of time over which it is administered (acute versus chronic), and the age, sex, and health of an organism. Nevertheless, the appearance or magnitude of an effect of any substance is tied to its dose. Hazard, therefore, can be thought of as a substance's dose-related array of possible deleterious effects on an organism of a specific age, gender, and health status exposed via oral, dermal, and/or inhalational pathways.

Should the knowledge that a substance is hazardous, i.e., potentially harmful under a specific set of circumstances, precipitate a corresponding (and urgent) reaction to do something about it? We are cautious by nature and thus want to be careful when we have knowledge of potential harm. The problem is knowing the appropriate amount of resources (financial, intellectual, etc.) to expend on managing what may be only potential harm, since—because hazard is contextual—it may never be manifested, or it may be manifested only under the most extreme conditions of chemical use.

To judge just how worried we should be about a toxicant in the environment, and therefore allocate the appropriate attention to its hazardousness, we have to understand the risk of adverse effect. Risk is also contextual, but a simple definition is the probability (likelihood) that adverse effects would occur under a specific situation or set of conditions. Often, regulatory toxicologists will express risk as a function of toxicity and exposure. Thus, risk is the probability or likelihood that the array of known hazards of a substance will actually occur if or when an organism is exposed. If exposure is nonexistent, then the likelihood of an effect is nil. If exposure does occur, then the likelihood of the substance being a hazard is conditioned not only on the dose but also on the age, gender, and health of that organism as well as the specific route of exposure. The important point is that the risk of adverse effects after exposure to a substance may be low or high, depending on all the factors affecting the hazards of that substance.

Thresholds

Low levels of exposure, even to a highly potent toxicant, may have a low probability of causing an adverse effect. In any case of exposure, whether through skin contact, inhalation, or oral ingestion, a number of physiological processes occur to modulate the dose or concentration of toxicant arriving at the cellular level, and thus the probability of interaction with enzymes or receptors. All of these physiological processes that determine what amount of toxicant arrives at the site of the cell enzymes or receptors is described by pharmacokinetics. Pharmacokinetic studies examine rate and extent of chemical uptake processes following dermal, oral, and inhalational exposures. The amount of toxicant entering into the systemic circulation (bloodstream) is studied and then followed to its subsequent distribution among all body regions down to the cellular level. The toxicant amount changes as it is degraded by enzyme systems and excreted (sometimes unaltered) from the body. Whatever toxicant is left over from all these pharmacokinetic processes arrives at the site of the potential enzymes or receptors complementary enough in structure to have any probability of interaction. The specific interactions are called pharmacodynamics.

The combination of pharmacokinetic processes and the kinetics of pharmacodynamic interactions may result in adverse physiological effects. Generally speaking, the physiological systems most often studied are the nervous and endocrine system, although the immune system is necessarily included because these three systems communicate with one another.

Figure 6. Typical monotonic relationship between increasing dose (or concentration) and population response.

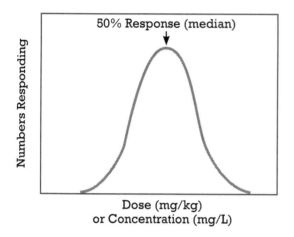

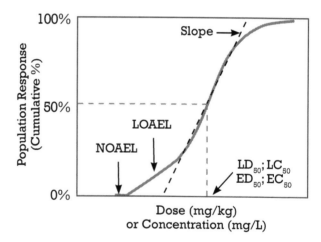

The relationship can be expressed as the numbers responding to any given dose metric. If the numbers are transformed to the cumulative proportion (i.e., percent) of the population responding, then an 'S'-shaped curve results, which can be described by a logistic mathematical function. At some dose, no measurable response is observed, and this dose is designated the no observable adverse effect level (NOAEL) or concentration (NOAEC). The LOAEL represents the dose at which an adverse effect is statistically significantly different from the response in the control. The LD50 and ED50 represent the median response in the population (i.e., 50% response) for either lethality (L) or any other measured response (E).

Researchers studying the interaction of toxicants with whole animals (*in vivo* studies) or with animal tissues, cells, and macromolecules (*in vitro* studies) attempt to establish a threshold for a physiological or biochemical reaction. They use a wide range of doses (exposures) and concentrations. The threshold is often reported as an empirical dose level in which no observable adverse effect (i.e., the NOAEL) occurs. To determine the NOAEL, however, the researcher must expose an animal to sufficiently high concentrations to see what a typical response looks like. The dose just causing a reaction is called the LOAEL (lowest observable adverse effects level). For any one specific response, the proportion of animals responding forms a monotonic functional relationship with the dose that is mathematically depicted as an S-shaped curve (Figure 6). For any effect, therefore, the researcher can estimate the proportion of the population responding to a particular dose. Similarly, the researcher can estimate when no responses in a population will occur.

The type of experiment that allows construction of the aforementioned dose-response curves and determination of a no-effects threshold falls under the rubric of regulatory toxicology. These experiments are most useful for assessing risk of an adverse effect following exposure under environmental conditions. Furthermore, experiments that attempt to define a threshold for an effect are quite different in objective than experiments that are designed to understand the mechanism of an effect. These latter experiments dominate the published toxicology literature today. However, those experiments necessarily use high enough doses so that an effect is always manifested and can therefore be studied. Although informative from the perspective of a basic biochemical understanding, mechanistic experiments are not very useful for characterizing the risk of effects following chemical exposure in the environment (i.e., outside of the laboratory).

In summary, then, the toxicity of a chemical is an inherent property related to its structural ability to interact with some complementary enzyme or receptor in a cell. If the structures are highly complementary, such that the probability of interaction is high, then the toxicant is considered highly potent; but if structural complementarity is low, the toxicant has low potency.

Regardless of potency, pharmacokinetic processes modify the probability of pharmacodynamic interactions, and thus all toxicants have thresholds for an effect. Pertinently, these interactions and thresholds apply to all chemicals, natural and synthetic, because all are under control of the fundamental laws of thermodynamics and kinetics.

Endocrine Disruption: Is It Just Hormonal?

Myth: Consideration of endocrine disruption changes the paradigm of what we know about pesticide effects. "Dose makes the poison" is no longer relevant because pesticides affect the endocrine system at levels equivalent to environmental exposures.

The Reality: Confusion Between a Changing Paradigm and a Shift in Focus, Away from Cancer, to a Different Physiological System

In the history of biology, those remembered by posterity are individuals who have created a paradigm shift in thinking about fundamental life process-es. Perhaps at the pinnacle of paradigm shifters is Charles Darwin. Indeed, an often-quoted paraphrase is "nothing in biology makes sense except in the light of evolution" (Dobzhansky 1964), and of course we have Darwin to thank for generating a line of inquiry leading to the modern theory of biological evolution. Cracking the genetic code, following the discovery of the structure of DNA, resulted in a plethora of new methods to study how life works at the molecular level. Of course, as we study different levels of organization, from cells to tissues to organs to whole organisms, new properties emerge that are increasingly difficult to describe in simple molecular terms.

In the context of biological history, perhaps we shouldn't be surprised that some researchers would enjoy being called paradigm shifters. However, changing the focus of study from one physiological system to another is not a paradigm shift, because all possible interactions of toxicants in the 'new' system are still constrained by fundamental laws of thermodynamics and kinetics. More specifically, over the last several decades, toxicological focus has shifted from carcinogenic responses to endocrine system responses. Whereas the 1950s through the 1980s focused on carcinogenic mechanisms largely tied to interactions with the genome, during the time between the late 1980s and now, focus has shifted to chemicals (synthetic and natural) and their interactions with receptors of the endocrine system. At first, the estrogen receptor, owing to intense interest in reproductive biology, was the object of most scrutiny, but now the testosterone (i.e., androgen) and thyroid receptors have been thrown into the mix.

A handful of studies putatively indicating that chemicals at very low levels of exposure could result in endocrine-mediated alterations in tissues of neonatal rodents, especially male prostate gland structure, suggested that a new perspective on toxicants was needed (vom Saal et al. 1997). Of course, one's perception of what constitutes a low dose requires tempering by how the dose is administered and a query as to whether the "specified" dose was chosen, because any dose lower would not result in the measured effect at all. In addition to observations of a slight difference in male prostate gland weight between dosed and control animals (vom Saal et al. 1997), as one example of an endocrine system paradigm-changing effect, the dose-response relationship accompanying the observation was nonmonotonic. In other words, the observed effects on gland weight did not vary in a lockstep linear fashion with increasing doses (Figure 7). The highest dose caused loss of gland weight and mid-doses caused increase in gland weight. The validity of the conclusions of these early reports has been questioned on grounds of statistical inadequacies (Haseman et al. 2001) or

Figure 7. Effects of DES (diethylstilbestrol) on mouse prostate gland weight measured eight months after birth.

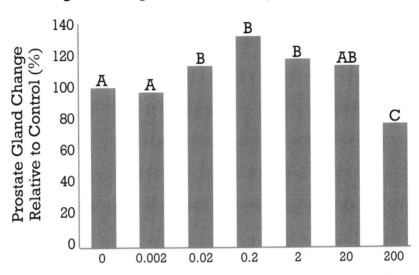

DES, a drug given to reduce miscarriages during the 1960s, and also used as a stimulatory hormone in cattle feed, has a potency similar in magnitude to that of estradiol. This graph is based on the one presented in vom Saal et al. (1997) that arguably initiated concerns about nonmonotonic effects of hormonally active agents. The data are shown as percentage change in gland weight relative to the control (100%), and the graph has been rescaled to start from zero change. Bars with the same letters are not significantly different from one another (probably < 0.05). Ignoring the lack of difference between prostate gland changes at doses of 0.002 and 20 µg/kg, the graph is considered nonmonotonic in trend because, at some doses, prostate gland weight growth is stimulated, but at the highest dose it is inhibited, suggesting onset of cytotoxicity.

have been judged inconclusive, imprecise, and of uncertain biological relevance (Melnick et al. 2002). Nevertheless, the problem in interpreting nonmonotonic responses arises when two different physiological phenomena are actually being measured by the same endpoint, such as gland weight changes. For example, no pathology other than gland weight changes may occur at low doses, but at high doses toxicity may set in and gland weight changes are actually due to a different phenomenon, such as greatly increased cell death.

Regardless of the cause of a nonmonotonic response (assuming the same physiological response is actually being measured on each side of the dosage range), receptor (e.g., estrogen receptor) interactions with ligands (e.g., estrogen or a toxicant) are governed by the principles of biochemical kinetics. Thus, the paradigm has not shifted; concentration of the ligand still influences receptor-ligand complexation. Kinetic analyses of molecule-molecule interactions can show the probability of those interactions as a function of dose (or concentration). An illustration of this concept can help dispel the myth that low doses from environmental exposures of hormonally active agents are inordinately hazardous. Thus, Figure 8 shows that ligand-receptor complexes, the kinetic mechanism initiating a hormonally induced physiological response, are incredibly low if the ligand concentration is low. Similarly, ligand-receptor interactions are reduced and slowed down as a chemical's potency decreases (Figure 9). Therefore, no paradigm has really shifted. Recall the premise that mechanistic studies are not designed to show the threshold level of plausible effects. Yet reexamination of Figure 7 does show a definitive threshold (i.e., at 0.002 µg/kg), even for the drug DES, arguably of similar or greater potency to estrogen in binding to the estrogen receptor (Okluicz and Leavitt 1988; Hendry et al. 1999, 2004).

Figure 8. Receptor-ligand interactions.

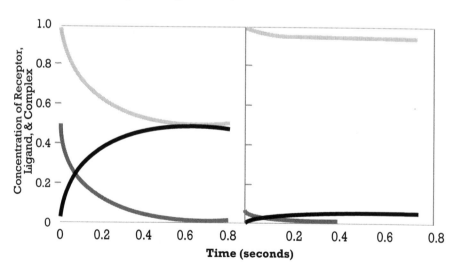

Vetting and Regulating Pesticides

Myth: We know very little about the effects of pesticides. EPA registers pesticides without fully considering all of their adverse effects.

The Reality of Pesticide Regulation in the U.S.: An Example of Moving the Precautionary Principle from Idealistic Philosophy to Real World Implementation

Analytical technology to detect chemical residues in the environment, including our own bodies, has advanced by orders of magnitude over the last 60 years (Figure 10). Before the introduction of specialized instruments such as GC-MS (gas chromatography-mass spectrometry) and LC-MS (liquid chromatography-mass spectrometry) became available to everyone's benchtop, identifying and quantifying environmental residues of chemicals was a slow and imprecise process that basically worked on one chemical entity at a time.

Often, only concentrations of chemicals equivalent to parts per thousand, or perhaps tens of parts per million, could be detected. Today, routine measurements are finding anthropogenic chemicals in the environment at levels of parts per trillion and even parts per quadrillion. Perhaps comprehension of the small magnitude of these minuscule amounts has been tainted by repeated reports of extraordinary congressional spending of billions of dollars. To place our abilities in perspective, 1 part per trillion of any compound found in water is equivalent to a purity of 99.9999999999% (Felsot 1998). The accuracy of quantifying such a level of contamination strains analytical abilities. Yet, a report of this level of contamination often provokes a cacophony of calls for more regulatory responsibility. On this basis, EPA is often criticized for inadequately regulating pesticides, perhaps because, historically, we have focused analytical efforts on them and can detect their residues in food and water. Ironically, monitoring pesticide residues routinely has grown out of intense regulation, not lax regulation.

Historically, regulation of pesticides grew out of laws during the first decade of the 20th century (Pure Food Act of 1906 and Insecticide Act of 1910). These laws eventually evolved by congressional statute into the Federal Food, Drug, and Cosmetic Act (FFDCA) and the Federal Insecticide, Fungicide, and Rodenticide Act (FIFRA). These two federal statutes operate in parallel to one another, but frequently they are just thought of as FIFRA only. During 1972, FIFRA administration was transferred to EPA from the USDA (U.S. Department of Agriculture), while the FDA still had authority under the FFDCA.

FIFRA has been amended many times by Congress to improve its oversight of chemical safety in the registration process, as well as to control better use of pesticide technology. The epitome of all amendments was born with the 1996 passage of the Food Quality Protection Act (FQPA). The FQPA was a milestone in regulating pesticide technology because, for the first time the law was mandated to be concerned only about risks of pesticide residues to consumers rather than benefits to farmers, and by extrapolation, to society. To implement such a change in perspective, Congress mandated that EPA examine more closely whether a chemical might be more hazardous to children than to adults, and to consider during registration of pesticide ingredients whether children's

Figure 9. Receptor Ligand Interactions.

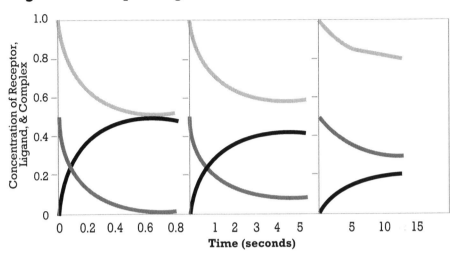

The graphs depict three different chemicals, each with a different affinity to a specific receptor. The middle graph and right graph depict ligands that are approximately 10 and 100 times less potent than the ligand depicted in the graph on the left. These interactions with compounds of different potencies illustrate that the receptor is not only quantitatively less bound as potency decreases, but the time for binding to occur is also slowed down. Both effects would lower the probability of an adverse effect.

exposure might be higher than that of adults. EPA would have to change its exposure analyses to include all sources of exposure beyond food, such as from chemical residues in drinking water and from home and garden use. Thus pesticide residues in water, soil, air, and vegetation became important in assessing risk to human health in addition to the historical focus on food.

Congress also told EPA that they must consider for registration decisions whether a chemical was hormonally active in the endocrine system. Cancer potential was also reemphasized but somewhat downplayed by the new concerns about putative "disruption" of the endocrine system by exogenous chemical residues, whether synthetic or naturally occurring. Finally, EPA would have to develop procedures for cumulating exposure to multiple pesticide residues if the pharmacodynamics of the specific pesticides were

Figure 10. Analytical Technology Has Advanced Faster than Biological Understanding

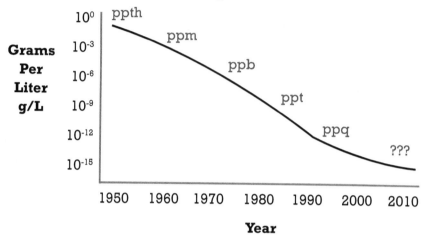

Depiction of change in detection limits (1 ppm = 10^{-3} g/L) over the last 60 years of contaminant monitoring. For year 2010, uncertainty is expressed owing to the unreliability of detections reported at parts per quadrillion (ppq) and lack of articles reporting detections lower than 1 part per trillion (ppt).

identical. In short, the FQPA was a regulatory paradigm shift. Nevertheless, the basic procedure of collecting toxicological and exposure data remained in effect, perhaps with the exception of greater focus on measuring parameters that could reflect endocrine system effects. Furthermore, the objective of assembling the data for risk assessment has remained the operational paradigm for making regulatory decisions to register a chemical for use as a pesticide.

The history of pesticide regulation in the U.S. gives evidence of the law actually being a form of the precautionary approach in operation. For example, the regulations written by EPA are vetted publicly for comment, with EPA responding directly to all stakeholders. The regulations are dynamic and respond to new concerns. Testing and data collection is funded by developers of the technology who are requesting registration. The data is audited for quality assurance by agents independent of the owners of the pesticide technology. The raw data are independently assessed by EPA for risk of adverse effects.

After a registration and commercialization, the technology is continuously monitored from the viewpoint of new toxicological information and residue amounts present in the environment. This activity is shared by all stakeholders, including EPA, industry, academia, and even environmental advocacy groups. The law prescribes that any adverse effects findings or reports be turned over by industry to EPA (CFR 1997). In making decisions to register, re-register, or decline registration of a pesticide, EPA can and does consider whether safer products are already on the market, or if the new product will replace an older, more hazardous product. Thus, modern pesticide law in the U.S. meets the idealism of the precautionary approach (Tickner 2002): it is increasingly based only on analysis of hazard; it is democratic, involving many stakeholders; it meets the "polluter pays" principle; it's dynamic and changes to accommodate new information; it monitors the effects of the decisions to register a product; and it is set up to encourage development and commercialization of incrementally safer products.

The Reality of Pesticide Regulation: Truckloads of Data on Every Conceivable Effect from Studies with Overlapping and Redundant Objectives

As delineated in Figure 11, the prime objective of modern pesticide law is setting a tolerance, also known worldwide as a maximum residue limit (MRL), for pesticide residues in foods. In fact, FDA and USDA testing shows no detectable pesticide residues in the majority of all foods (FDA 2009, USDA AMS 2010). When detected, insecticide residues specifically occur disproportionately in less than half of commercial fruits. Few fungicides are detected, and almost no herbicide residues are detected. Nevertheless, despite the setting of a tolerance for pesticide residues in food as a requirement of registration, all toxicological and environmental chemistry studies are brought to bear on the task. Thus, a full-blown risk assessment is required for every pesticide, no matter what the end use is. Even if a pesticide is oriented for home use, the toxicological and environmental data available are universally

Figure 11. Schematic Overview of Modern Laws
Regulating Pesticide Registration and Use

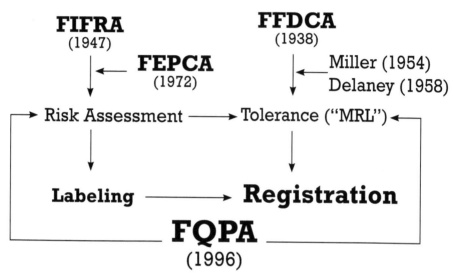

Both FIFRA (Federal Insecticide, Fungicide, Rodenticide Act) and FFDCA (Federal Food, Drug, Cosmetic Act) arguably evolved from earlier laws known as the Insecticide Act (1910) and the Pure Food Act (1906), respectively. The laws work in parallel under the direction of EPA. Both have been amended many times (e.g., Miller Amendment; Delaney Amendment), with the latest major amendment being the Food Quality Protection Act (1996). The FEPCA (the Federal Environmental Pesticide Control Act) essentially created a risk management standard of "reasonable certainty of no harm" to the environment and workers. The FQPA basically changed the historic risk-benefits balancing of FIFRA to a risk consideration only; furthermore, they broadened consumer-exposure analysis to include residential use of products in addition to food and water. Schematic reprinted from Felsot 2010.

required. The difference is that, for agricultural use, certain exposure assumptions are made, while for home use, other, more appropriate exposure routes are assumed.

Given that the requirement for risk assessment data is monolithic, regardless of how a pesticide might be used, the types of studies are well designed in order to acquire the most useful and informative data. Thus, the general protocol requirements for all tests needed to assess human health effects and, likewise,

Table 3. EPA Harmonized Test Guidelines requirements (EPA 2010).

Test Series Number	Test Guidelines Series Identification Grouping	Number of Individual Tests in the Series
810	Product Performance	8
830	Product Properties	35
835	Fate, Transport & Transformation	42
840	Spray Drift	2
850	Ecological Effects	51
860	Residue Chemistry	17
870	Health Effects	49
875	Occupational & Residential Exposure	13
880	Biochemicals	7
885	Microbial Pesticide[s]	41
890	Endocrine Disruptor Screening Program	11

Each new pesticide data package will be required to address the individual test detailed in each section of the test guidelines, unless EPA waives the test owing to lack of relevance or, in the case of re-registrations, availability of sufficient data in the files.

ecological effects, are accessible to the public through EPA Office of Chemical Safety and Pollution Prevention (OCSPP) web site known as the Harmonized Test Guidelines (http://www.epa.gov/ocspp/pubs/frs/home/guidelin.htm) (Table 3). The total number of tests for all aspects of the chemicals proposed for registration is 276. However, 50 of the tests pertain only to pesticides classified as 'biochemical', which are typically natural products and pesticides developed from microorganisms (i.e., microbial pesticides). Thus, over 220 different tests on conventional chemical pesticides are required before registration. Of this total, 49 tests address a wide array of health effects, and 51 address ecological effects. 11 test protocol guidelines have been issued specifically for endocrine effects.

The tests for a wide array of physiological effects on the nervous and immune system are covered under the Health Effects Test Guidelines. These tests focus on acute toxicity (from a single high exposure) to effects from repeated exposures over the life span of the test animals. The array of measurements includes, but is not limited to, reproductive and developmental effects (which also are indicative of endocrine system effects [Stevens et al. 1997]), multiple generation effects, carcinogenicity, and blood enzyme levels.

The test animals are usually rodents, but for older chemicals, beagle dogs also have been used to supplement the rodent tests. The rodents are always tested in groups by gender, and frequent measurements are made to assess specific parameters and general well-being of the test animals. Pertinently, the tests that EPA relies on most for characterizing the risk of adverse effects are the 90-day and 2-year continuous feeding studies. In these subchronic and chronic exposure tests, respectively, a rodent is exposed through diet to a test chemical at the stated dosage every day. Thus, each day the amount of food eaten is recorded so that the exact daily dose can be monitored throughout the study. In addition to frequent monitoring of animals for signs of overt toxicity, the animals are sacrificed at the end of the study to generate thousands of tissue specimens for examination.

Whose Data Are They?

Under mandates of the FIFRA and the FFDCA, manufacturers seeking registration of new pesticide products or re-registration of older products must submit data that covers the required subject areas in the Harmonized Test Guidelines (Table 3). These studies are best characterized as regulatory toxicology because they are intended to discover thresholds of toxicity for an array of adverse effects. Most of the toxicity tests use three dosages and a non-dosed control group (typically rodents and beagle dogs). Based on preliminary range-finding studies, the dosages are chosen so that most will define a specific but observed NOAEL, with the next two doses likely producing some measurable effect.

Regulatory toxicology tests differ fundamentally from more basic research in that the latter is designed to study mechanisms of effects but not necessarily thresholds of effects. Although chemical manufacturers may also carry out basic research once they have discovered a potential commercially useful product, most research is carried out at public institutions (e.g., NIH and EPA labs) and universities. The studies are designed so that definitive reactions are observed but often do not define thresholds for the reactions as do regulatory studies. Basic research could be useful for identifying hazards under the context of the specific laboratory conditions, but they are not useful for risk characterization because they do not seek a NOAEL.

Another major difference between basic toxicological research carried out by chemical manufacturers and universities or public institutions is that the former are required to conduct all studies according to Good Laboratory Practice (GLP) standards. GLP standards allow EPA to independently audit the generation of all pieces of data, as well as determine if studies were conducted according to pre-written protocols. Thus, every "data point" is tracked, audited, and validated. Such meticulous attention to validating data and ensuring compliance with written protocols is not a requirement for grant-funded research. For this reason, EPA often does not use research not conducted under GLPs to make regulatory decisions about pesticide registrations. However, EPA uses the basic research to inform the agency of new issues or peculiarities when testing responses that may need more scrutiny.

How EPA Determines Safety Under the Mandates of the Law

With piles of data at hand, EPA first validates its origin and then uses the raw data to conduct its own risk characterizations. EPA follows the long used and vetted tenets of risk characterization that involve problem formulation followed by the steps of hazard identification, dose-response assessment, exposure assessment, and risk characterization. The latter defines the risk by integrating exposure and the toxicological endpoint or benchmark of concern defined in the dose-response assessment.

Of the array of all types of effects that EPA examines, the agency looks for the one that has occurred at the lowest dose tested. The NOAEL from such a study is then used as the benchmark level from which to compare possible exposures to the pesticide. For example, many herbicides in the sulfonylurea class are of such low toxicity that exposure to hundreds or thousands of milligrams per kilogram of body weight are required to produce any effect. Often such effects are increased loss of body weight in females compared to the non-dosed population. Thus, simple body weight loss becomes the endpoint of concern and is then used to characterize risk. More specific effects can be measured when organophosphorus (OP) insecticides are tested. Specifically, this group of compounds inhibits the neurotransmitter-degrading enzyme acetylcholinesterase in the central nervous system. This effect is quite specific and due to a known singular biochemical mechanism (Mileson et al. 1998). So, for assessing safety of OP insecticides, EPA would choose enzyme inhibition as the most sensitive endpoint of toxicological concern. To reiterate, hazard identification characterizes the array of possible adverse effects, and dose-response assessment defines the thresholds for an effect and determines which effect specifically becomes the toxicological endpoint of concern. The philosophy behind this methodology is that, if you protect nontarget organisms from the most sensitive effect (i.e., the effect occurring at the lowest dose), then you can protect them from all other effects.

Once the most sensitive endpoint is chosen, then EPA applies uncertainty factors (a.k.a. safety factors) to ensure that any potential exposures are likely to be at least 100-fold lower than the NOAEL. One type of risk management device is called the RfD (reference dose), which is obtained by dividing the NOAEL (units of mg/kg/day) by 100. Next, EPA examines the database of pesticide residues in food and models an estimate of drinking water residues. EPA then compares the exposure to the NOAEL, concluding either that exposure is below the RfD or exceeds the RfD. If the estimated exposure exceeds the RfD, then EPA will demand some mitigation, such as restricting certain product uses or, in rare cases, refusing registration.

Some Case Studies: Reports of Hazards Do Not Reflect Risks

The next several sections examine more closely three specific pesticides (atrazine, chlorpyrifos, glyphosate) and the homologous group of pyrethroids in order to determine the validity of claims of imminent harm.

These pesticides were first registered by EPA 30-50 years ago but are still commonly used. Owing to their widespread use, more toxicological and epidemiological testing focusing on these compounds has arguably been conducted and published than on any other currently registered pesticide. Many of the published tests have examined few doses and were not designed to develop NOAELs for risk assessment, but often the researchers have extrapolated the adverse responses to human exposure. Few papers have challenged the results of these extrapolations on the basis of fundamental toxicological principles operational at the likely environmental or worker-associated exposures. Thus, choosing these highly studied pesticides offered an opportunity to examine critically the dosing regimes and biological plausibility of the purported effects in light of realistic exposures.

In reviewing the literature of these compounds, we deliberately avoided EPA analysis in order to determine if just relying on the open scholarly literature itself could lead to a more skeptical attitude toward claims of adverse effects. In every case, the main concerns about health or ecological impacts are explained, and rebuttals are made using the peer-reviewed literature. However, EPA-regulatory reference doses or generally acceptable acute toxicity parameters are used as background for comparative perspectives about the chemical's safety.

Atrazine

To call atrazine the "DDT" of herbicides would not be a hyperbolic exaggeration if a number of newspaper stories and research articles are added up. For example, searching Google Scholar for journal research articles yields over 58,000 hits on atrazine but 268,000 on DDT. This four-fold difference, however, reflects DDT's development and widespread use as an insecticide in the 1940s in contrast to atrazine's later development and commercialization, in the late 1950s. However, the comparison remains apt, considering the growing number of articles ascribing to atrazine ever more adverse effects, as have long been reported for DDT. Also, atrazine has long supplanted DDT as the most frequently detected pesticide in the environment, albeit not in food, where it is hardly ever found. One big difference between DDT and atrazine can be expressed by the following analogy: DDT is to bird declines as atrazine is to frogs' sexual development. But is it true? And, should atrazine be judged solely by frogs, as if this taxon were the proverbial canary in the coal mine? The concerns about atrazine generally divide between potential chronic effects on human health and effects on diminishing frog populations through disruption of the endocrine system.

In separating the myths and realities of atrazine toxicity, hazards, and risks, knowing that it was first registered in 1958, and thereafter intensively used mainly in corn production throughout the Western world, should lend some perspective to the most recent reports suggesting that the compound poses a risk to human health as well as to amphibians. Given the massive amounts and intensive use of atrazine in the Corn Belt over the last 50 years, new risk concerns seem odd because problems should have been noticeable within a short time after atrazine's commercialization. The reason for this conclusion is that atrazine was first reported in water wells and potable water supplies in the early 1970s (Richard et al. 1975). Once scientists start looking for a needle in the haystack, they usually will find it—but not because it wasn't present in the environment from the beginning of use.

Based on our current knowledge of the environmental chemodynamics of soil-applied chemicals, atrazine is likely to have worked its way into shallow ground water of the Corn Belt after the first year of use. Furthermore, atrazine residues are not being increasingly detected in the environment because use is increasing. In fact, use has gone down, if not remained stable. However, atrazine detection frequency is a classic story of detection sensitivity improvements (Kolpin 1995), not an indication of an exponential increase in residues entering the environment. Thus, contemporary stories raising alarms about atrazine in water supplies are just not plowing new ground but repeating information known for a very long time. The question about residues in water, especially drinking water supplies, generally raises the question of whether humans are adversely affected. The answer to this question rests on understanding atrazine's toxicology and the potential for exposure based on residues found in environments relevant to drinking water.

According to EPA, atrazine is considered to be of low toxicity, having an LD50 from single oral exposures of 1,869 mg/kg and dermal exposures of >2000 mg/kg (EPA 2002a). Its acute reference dose was developed by EPA as 0.10 mg/kg (EPA 2002b). Pertinently, this regulatory benchmark was based on highly dosed rodents, wherein an effect on bone development occurred at a dose rate of 70 mg/kg/day, but no effect occurred at 10 mg/kg/day. Among all the tests that were conducted, 10 mg/kg/day was the lowest dose without any effect, and thus it was specifically designated as the NOAEL. Also pertinently, this NOAEL is at least two orders of magnitude greater than the estimated 95th percentile exposure of 0.09 mg/kg/day following mixing/ loading and application (Gammon et al. 2005). In fact, at levels of human exposure that potentially occur during legal rates of application of atrazine for control of weeds, the compound has only one known definitive mode of causing toxicity. Atrazine inhibits plant physiology by disrupting photosynthesis, specifically in a biochemical pathway called Photosystem II (Devine et al. 1993). Animals, however, do not possess biochemical pathways that atrazine, at possible environmental levels, could affect. The latter statement is not to deny that testing of highly exaggerated doses causes physiological effects, but how much is used and the likelihood of comparable exposures must always be weighed.

EPA integrated the results from toxicology tests with volumes of water drunk in a day by adults or children to yield a maximum contaminant level (MCL) of 3 μg/L (ppb). This regulatory rule was developed under the mandate of the Safe Drinking Water Act. Although developed back in ~1989, the regulatory standard of 3 ppb has not been altered since. Perhaps EPA was not motivated to change this standard over the last thirty years because toxicological information has not pointed to any problem not already covered in the experiments submitted by the registrants for risk characterization by EPA. Indeed, EPA (2010) has stated, "Based on all the available test data, the Agency's evaluation, and scientific peer review, atrazine is not likely to be a human carcinogen". Because both rodent studies and available human epidemiology studies using workers handling atrazine failed to show any relationship between atrazine dose and cancer, EPA seems to be practicing the precautionary principle in asking for more epidemiological data. Yet the EPA has stated its skepticism for finding any correlations. The ongoing multi-year National Cancer Institute study called the Agricultural Health Study concluded in 2004, "Our analyses did not find any clear associations between atrazine exposure and any cancer analyzed" (Rusiecki et al. 2004). Such a conclusion is remarkable, given that nearly every study in the AHS consortium claims that there is an association between some pesticide and cancer or several other health effects. Significantly, the AHS study includes a cohort of over 70,000 pesticide workers and adult family members in Iowa and North Carolina. Thus, the pesticide users represent farms associated with grain production (corn and soybeans) and specialty crops (diversity of fruit and vegetables that are grown in the mid Atlantic region). Further concerns about atrazine's adversely affecting human health via chronic exposure were most recently dispelled by the World Health Organization. WHO (2010) is recommending a drinking water quality guideline for atrazine of 100 μg/L, a value notably higher than all previous guidelines.

Atrazine residues are not found in food, given that the chemical is applied directly to the soil of basically only one crop (i.e., corn) (USDA AMS 2009), so the only contemporary pathway of exposure would be drinking water derived ultimately from field runoff or subsurface drainage in the Corn Belt. Thus, a very limited geographically located population of consumers would be comparatively most exposed if atrazine residues survive water treatment and appear in finished drinking water supplies. Given that the MCL is based on a non-cancer endpoint that took into consideration the results of reproductive and developmental toxicity tests that would indicate endocrine system effects, a logical question is *how likely is it that people will be exposed to the MCL?* Remembering that the MCL has applied to it a very large safety factor of 1,000 (Richards and Baker 1995), one should be aware that even studies in the 1990s concluded that very few people (perhaps less than 1 person in 1,000) would be exposed to atrazine near the MCL (Richards and Baker 1995). The picture has only improved, with atrazine detectable concentrations in water dropping since 1996—due in part to changes in use rates and practices (Sullivan et al. 2009). The picture should become increasingly clear as even less atrazine is used with new hybrids of corn that resist glyphosate or other herbicides, thereby further reducing the need for atrazine.

The California EPA's independent study of likely human health effects from consumer and worker exposure to atrazine essentially concluded very little risk, largely because exposure was so low relative to effects seen in animal testing (Gammon et al. 2005). Although human exposure to atrazine seems to be insufficient to warrant concerns for risk to health, residue levels sometimes found in the water are putatively causing ecological effects through disruption of amphibian endocrine physiology. Addressing the question of whether frogs are being sexually transformed by exposure to low levels of atrazine in the environment first requires a determination of the basis for concern regarding frog development. The second consideration would take into account the likelihood of a frog being exposed to "low" levels of atrazine. Without a consideration of both factors, the risk cannot be placed in the context of human concerns.

Atrazine toxicity is very low to virtually all aquatic organisms except perhaps plants (which it is designed to kill), as shown in the accumulation of studies by EPA during the compound's reregistration process. For example, most aquatic organisms do not die unless concentrations approach mg/L levels (EPA 2002c; Solomon et al. 1996). To place this concentration in perspective, atrazine is found most frequently in water at levels between 0.001 and 1 μg/L.

While EPA is only now requiring that amphibians be tested, reports of effects of atrazine on gonadal development appeared in the early 2000s, a time of non-regulatory testing. Specifically, several papers exposed the African claw-toed frog (*Xenopus laevis*) to atrazine in water at levels ranging from 0.1 μg/L to 100 μg/L. The most cited report (Hayes et al. 2002) suggested that frogs were becoming feminized. In this case, feminization was measured as either the occurrence of oocytes in male testis tissue or a reduction in size of pharyngeal muscle that aids male frog sexual calling. A follow up study also showed the presence of oocytes in testis tissue, along with testicular dysgenesis (Hayes et al. 2003). However, in the latter study, no correlations were found between the intensity of the putative endocrine system effect and levels of atrazine in aquatic systems where the frogs were collected. Furthermore, frog populations from across eight regions in the U.S. under scrutiny seemed to be quite healthy, as determined from population abundance observations. However, a more recent study (Hayes et al. 2010) of sexual transformation from male to female upon exposure to atrazine in the lab has stirred popular media headlines, as have earlier studies.

If science made definitive conclusions about the ways of the world based on only one laboratory, the chances for misunderstanding a natural phenomenon would be quite high. For this reason, that different laboratories try to repeat each other's work is preferable in order to determine whether observations are generalizable across species or are even likely in the actual environment. Thus, other independent laboratory studies of the effect of atrazine on frog gonadal development, both of *Xenopus* and several other species, have failed to repeat the observations of Hayes et al. (2002, 2003) (Carr et al. 2003; Coady et al. 2004, 2005; Du Preez et al. 2008; Kloas et al. 2008; Oka et al. 2009; Spolyarich et al. 2010). Field studies also do not find positive correlations between atrazine concentrations in breeding habitats and adverse histological or sex ratio patterns (Du Preez et al. 2005, 2009; Smith et al. 2005; McDaniel et al. 2008).

In addition to a number of studies failing to conclude that atrazine is affecting gonadal development of frogs, these studies have generally made two important points that should substantially lessen any concerns about atrazine functioning as an endocrine disrupting chemical. First, the putative mechanism by which Hayes et al. (2002, 2005) have proposed that atrazine feminizes male frogs works through aromatase enzyme induction. Induction of the enzyme could result in greater rates of transformation of testosterone to estradiol, thus depleting male androgen hormone concentrations during key stages of development. However, studies that do not show any hormonally related effects of atrazine also fail to detect any induction of aromatase. (Hecker et al. 2004, 2005; Murphy et al. 2006; Oka et al. 2008). Male frogs collected from agriculturally-dominated habitats do not show significant differences in estradiol hormone levels or estradiol/testosterone ratios from non-agricultural landscapes (McCoy et al. 2008). Hormone levels in frogs collected from diverse non-agricultural and agricultural habitats did not, in fact, correlate with atrazine levels (McDaniel et al. 2008). Thus, little support for a hypothesis of aromatase induction has been observed in studies that relate field-collected frog parameters to atrazine residues.

The second informative point is atrazine's lack of effect on reproductive success. Thus, allowing exposed tadpoles to complete development and then mate results in no impairment of fecundity or fertility (Du Preez et al. 2008). So, even if atrazine were having a non-detectable effect on frogs, the ecological consequences are moot, owing to a lack of effect on fertility. Indeed, this laboratory observation echoes what Hayes et al. (2003) observed in the field when they examined frogs across eight U.S. regions. To quote from the latter research, "Juvenile *R. pipiens* were abundant at all of our collection sites, however, including agricultural areas in Iowa and Nebraska. The abundance of frogs at these sites suggests that the effects are reversible, that some percentage of the population does not show this response, that these developmental abnormalities do not impair reproductive function at sexual maturity, and/or that continuously exposed populations have evolved resistance to atrazine."

More recent research has questioned whether frogs make good "canaries in the coal mine" (Kerby et al. 2010). In fact, the conclusions were that amphibians are not as sensitive to environmental contaminants as other aquatic organisms are. Thus, newspaper accounts that express alarm at the findings from one laboratory over atrazine's potential to disrupt the endocrine system, regarding these as a bellwether for human concern, seems to belie all the data that has been published within the last five years. Ironically, the same newspaper accounts of recent atrazine effects from the Hayes lab seemed to have forgotten their own publication two years earlier showing that frog populations were in much poorer condition around urban influenced aquatic systems than around agricultural systems (Barringer 2008). Given that atrazine is not permitted or used in urban settings, the facts from the environment contrast with one scientist's observations in the lab.

One thing is certain, however: Studies will continue on atrazine as long as it is used. Indeed, EPA is continuing to examine data on human cancer epidemiology, as well as effects on amphibians, noting in an April 2010 web posting, "Although EPA is not currently requiring additional testing of atrazine on amphibians, as discussed earlier on this Web page, EPA has begun a comprehensive reevaluation of atrazine's ecological effects, including potential effects on amphibians, based on data generated since 2007" (EPA 2011). No one can rightly claim that EPA is not practicing precaution when it comes to atrazine.

Chlorpyrifos

Chlorpyrifos is an organophosphorus ester insecticide (specifically, O,O-diethyl O-3,5,6-trichloro-2-pyridyl phosphorothioate) that was first commercialized in 1965. Before the passage of the FQPA in 1996, chlorpyrifos was arguably the most used insecticide in the world. By 2002, however, its use on developing fruit and as a termiticide and home and lawn insecticide had been voluntarily suspended by its manufacturer, Dow AgroSciences, in an agreement with EPA. Chlorpyrifos is still registered for some vegetable crops (e.g., plants in the Family Cruciferae, such as cabbage, collards, kale and Family Alliaceae —such as onions), including field and sweet corn, but its major use today is restricted to dormancy season sprays on pome fruits (apples and pears) and nuts. Dormant sprays occur when no fruit is growing; thus the opportunity for exposure through fruit and nut consumption is nil. Because potential chlorpyrifos hazards are dependent on the degree of exposure, examination of food residue data foretells the likelihood of adverse effects. Data from the USDA's most recently published comprehensive survey of pesticide residues, in distribution centers around the U.S., are informative for predicting trends. The latest data indicate that only 3% of more than 10,000 individual food items analyzed had detectable residues of chlorpyrifos (USDA AMS 2009). The levels found were typically 100-1000-fold less than the residue tolerance, or the legal concentration that has been set, in part, to protect human health as required under the Food Quality Protection Act (1996; Title IV, Section 405(b)(2)(A)(i and ii)).

Chlorpyrifos, like other organophosphorus esters, inhibits the nerve membrane enzyme called acetylcholinesterase (AChE). AChE breaks down the neurotransmitter acetylcholine, which functions as the signaling compound between nerve axons and dendrites in the central nervous system as the electrical current traveling down stimulated nerve membranes is transduced to chemical energy in the region of the synapse. AChE is anchored on the post-synaptic (i.e., dendritic) membranes near the acetylcholine receptor proteins. By breaking down and thus lowering the concentration of acetylcholine neurotransmitter before it can bind to the receptors, AChE functions to dampen the stimulatory electrical signals originating distally from up the nerve axon. When OP insecticides bind to the enzyme, they inhibit its function. Inhibition of AChE allows excessive concentrations of AChE to persist in the synapse and, consequently, stimulation of the nerve axons continues unabated.

Inhibition of AChE is the only known biochemical effect of chlorpyrifos at exposure levels associated with legal rates of application in the environment. However, chlorpyrifos itself is not functional in inhibiting acetylcholinesterase.

Rather, chlorpyrifos has to be metabolized to an oxidized form called chlor-pyrifos oxon to have biological activity. Therefore, of public health interest is whether chlorpyrifos oxon is detected in food. The USDA AMS (2009) reported no findings of oxon residues in food, thus validating very minimal exposure of human populations to chlorpyrifos. Athough chlorpyrifos can be metabolized to its oxon form within an organism, its further metabolism and excretion in humans is so fast that it cannot be detected even within hours after dosing (Timchalk et al. 2002).

Despite the low potential for current exposure of U.S. citizens to chlorpyrifos insecticide residues, the literature is replete with data showing widespread detection of an essentially nontoxic breakdown product called trichloropyridinol in human urine, as well as alkyl phosphate metabolites (Payne-Sturges et al. 2009). Thus, the perception that people today are widely exposed to chlorpyrifos residues is generated from these studies. However, these studies reflect the results from urine samples collected when chlorpyrifos was widely used and before the significant restrictions on its use. Furthermore, evidence suggests that the non-toxic alkyl phosphate metabolites occur already on the fruit before consumption (Zhang et al. 2008). Thus, detection of these chlorpyrifos degradation products in urine is not an accurate reflection of exposure to the toxicant. Because dietary exposure, rather than house dust, has been considered a primary pathway of exposure to children (Morgan et al. 2005), detection of chlorpyrifos residues in households is also not directly applicable to actual exposure levels. Thus, the present perception of hazards from chlorpyrifos (as well as the few other OP in-secticides still used), based on older studies of residues in households and urine biomonitoring, are inconsistent with the studies showing chlorpyrifos residues are only infrequently detected in food—as well as the fact that the compound is no longer used directly on fruit or in urban environments. Indeed, within two years after removal of chlorpyrifos from urban uses, researchers could detect lower exposures, concluding that aggregate potential doses of chlorpyrifos were well below published reference dose values (Wilson et al. 2010).

Any compound that affects any of the nervous system biochemical pa-rameters is considered automatically to be a neurotoxicant. As is true for all biochemicals, the probability of causing observable neurotoxic responses to chlorpyrifos and similar chemical compounds depends on dose, or the degree of exposure. When there is proven exposure in a case-controlled epidemiological study, the results do not support a case for hazardousness. For example, applicators of chlorpyrifos-based termiticides were logically a very exposed subset of the population. Thus, if chlorpyrifos is a potent neurotoxicant in adults, one would predict severe neurotoxicology problems in applicators. Yet, an epidemiological study of 191 applicators, whose urine proved they were over 100 times more exposed than a non-applicator control population, concluded, "The exposed group did not differ significantly from the nonexposed group for any test in the clinical examination. Few significant differences were found in nerve conduction velocity, arm/hand tremor, vibrotactile sensitivity, vision, smell, visual/motor skills, or neurobehavioral skills" (Steenland et al. 2000). The latter observational results would be considered more objective than questions seeking subjective information about applicators' personal experiences. The only subgroup where personal experiences regarding illness could be reliably measured were the eight applicators (of a total of 191) who had a past acute illness associated with chlorpyrifos use.

One concern about chlorpyrifos exposure voiced frequently in the literature is the potential neurotoxic effects on developing fetuses, newborns, and adolescents. Many of the reports suggesting potential effects in these vulnerable age groups stem from one research lab at Duke University starting in the 1990s and continuing through today, although other labs have reached similar conclusions (cf. literature reviews in Slotkin 1999; Eaton et al. 2008). Studies have included both *in vivo* exposure of neonate rat pups (e.g., Campbell et al. 1997; Whitney et al. 1995; Song et al. 1997; Dam et al. 1998, 1999; Aldridge et al. 2005a) and occasionally mothers (e.g., Qiao et al. 2003; Meyer et al. 2003; Aldridge et al. 2005b) and *in vitro* studies on axonal type cell cultures (e.g., Jameson et al. 2006; Yang et al. 2008; Slotkin et al. 2010). The conclusion of all of the aforementioned types of studies is that chlorpyrifos may cause developmental neurotoxicity through mechanisms other than through cholinergic effects (Slotkin et al. 2006).

Several issues are raised by the plethora of research on chlorpyrifos and putative mechanisms of development neurotoxicity, owing to the policy that EPA has adopted for regulating organophosphorus insecticides. Presently,

EPA regulates this group by defining the NOAEL for acetylcholinesterase inhibition. In particular for chlorpyrifos, however, a plasma-residing form of acetylcholinesterase, popularly called "pseudocholinesterase," or just plasma cholinesterase, is actually more sensitive to inhibition than true acetylcholinesterase, which is found in the central nervous system as well as in red blood cells (Eaton et al. 2008). Thus, inhibition of plasma cholinesterase is the most sensitive endpoint chosen to characterize risk and calculate an RfD. For example, based on the NOAEL for plasma cholinesterase inhibition and application of a 100-fold safety factor, EPA has set an RfD of 0.005 mg/kg/day for short-term (acute) chlorpyrifos exposure. To protect children under six years old, EPA included an additional 10-fold safety factor to yield a population-adjusted reference dose (called a PAD) of 0.0005 mg/kg/day). The comparable long-term (chronic) PAD, which included the combined 1000-fold safety factor, was designated as 0.00003 mg/kg/day. EPA's final decision for re-registration of chlorpyrifos in 2006 was predicated on no further urban uses and no uses on fruit trees post-bloom or on certain vegetables, like tomatoes (EPA 2006a). Pertinently, EPA uses the RfD as an exposure guideline to ensure the congressional mandate of "safe", meaning a "reasonable certainty that no harm will result from aggregate exposure to the pesticide chemical residue, including all anticipated dietary exposures and all other exposures for which there is reliable information" (Food Quality Protection Act 1996).

EPA cited the growing developmental neurotoxicity literature at the time of its reregistration decision, noting that a noncholinergic mechanism could be at work (i.e., a mechanism that does not inhibit acetylcholinesterase). The most recent literature based on *in vitro* studies suggests that acetylcholinesterase functions as a morphogen — i.e., the intact enzyme stimulates growth of nerve axons. Simple binding to the enzyme without inhibiting its activity could reduce this morphogenic functionality (Yang et al. 2008). Another proposed mechanism is the altered regulation of genes that code for neurotrophic factors that affect nerve growth (Slotkin et al. 2010). Although EPA did not consider these effects when delineating its RfD for protection of infants and children, a recent risk characterization for school children by the California Environmental Protection Agency proposed a child specific RfD of 0.0001 mg/kg/day after considering the noncholinergic mechanisms that may affect the developing central nervous system and applying a 300-fold safety factor to a NOAEL for such effects.

A second issue raised by a putative novel mechanism of action of chlorpyrifos, and perhaps other OP insecticides that are either no longer used or have very minimal usage today (i.e., parathion and diazinon, respectively), is what level of exposure for either pregnant mothers or newborns/infants might be associated with the developmental neurological effects. A disproportionate number of studies that have shown developmental effects through noncholinergic mechanisms have used exposure routes and dosages that do not reflect environmental reality. For example, many studies use subcutaneous injections of chlorpyrifos in dimethyl sulfoxide, a solvent that promotes rapid penetration through biological tissues (Pathan and Setty 2009). Furthermore, dosages of chlorpyrifos have ranged from about 0.5 mg/kg body weight to 1-5 mg/kg. The reality of exposures is that humans would be exposed as a fetus through the mother's placental barrier, or as an infant through mother's milk, or as a child through the food supply. Note that chlorpyrifos is no longer used around homes, so consideration of this specific route of exposure is not relevant to characterizing the remaining uses of chlorpyrifos. Also, exposure would be divided throughout any one day and not a single acute bolus, as occurs in many lab studies that focus on mechanisms of an effect rather than on likely risks of an effect. An analysis of the effect of route, vehicle, and divided doses on pharmacokinetics and concentrations of chlorpyrifos and metabolites in blood suggest that single bolus doses in vehicle (corn oil or dimethylsulfoxide) raise blood levels higher than levels from divided doses in the diet (Marty et al. 2007).

Although the routes of exposure and concentration in the preponderance of developmental neurotoxicity studies do not reflect reality, one could still use the data to determine whether chlorpyrifos exposures are likely to have the effects seen in neonatal laboratory animals. Such an analysis would require information about the likely intake of chlorpyrifos residues. The analysis would also benefit from information about blood and/or tissue levels of chlorpyrifos or its detoxification metabolite TCP (trichlorpyridinol) for comparison to effects observed during *in vitro* studies.

As part of its decision to re-register chlorpyrifos, EPA estimated the aggregate intake of residues if certain agricultural, and all urban uses, were to be curtailed. For example, such restricted use patterns of chlorpyrifos would result in a worst-case aggregate intake from food, water, and mosquito control use for children one to six years of age, of ~0.00067 mg/kg (EPA 2006a). Thus, EPA's estimated exposure for current use patterns of chlorpyrifos would be nearly 1000-fold lower than the lowest doses given to neonatal rats in many studies of developmental neurotoxicity. For example, in one study concluding that adverse neurodevelopmental effects follow gestational exposures, pregnant rats were dosed subcutaneousy by injection with 1-5 mg/kg chlorpyrifos (Aldridge et al. 2005b). Neonatal rats and post-natal rats were dosed by injection with one and five mg/kg, respectively.

Studies conducted *in vitro* using model cell cultures of nerve axon growth are not directly comparable to dosages from *in vivo* studies. One problem is that *in vitro* cell culture studies place the toxicant at the surface of cell membranes, an exposure situation that is completely devoid of all the pharmacokinetic mechanisms that would significantly reduce concentrations arriving at target sites through transport in the blood stream. However, the concentrations in *in vitro* studies can be compared to blood concentrations of chlorpyrifos or TCP that have been measured in association with known dosages either to neonates or to pregnant females.

To perform a risk characterization that would be conservatively protective in perspective, one should examine a study that has found an adverse effect at the lowest dose relative to other studies. Recently, a well-conducted study showed that axon growth by lengthening was reduced when cultured rat dorsal ganglion cells from the brainstem were exposed to 0.001 µM (equivalent to a chlorpyrifos concentration of 0.351 µg/L) (Yang et al. 2008). Although another study from the same lab showed no significant response until the concentration was 0.01 M, one could use 0.001 µM as a benchmark for comparison to what a fetus or neonate might have in its blood. One study showed that "fetuses of dams given 1 mg/kg/day had a blood CPF level of about 1.1 ng/g (0.0011 µg/g), but had no inhibition of ChE of any tissue" (Mattsson et al. 2000). Thus, this study proved that chlorpyrifos could be detected in blood without any cholinergic effects. If blood is assumed to have a density close to 1 g/mL, then 0.0011 µg/g translates to about 1 µg/L. Although a dose of 1 mg/kg is frequently described as "low" in the published literature, EPA estimated that worst-case aggregate exposures (i.e., food, water, and mosquito control combined) may be about 0.00067 mg/kg/day. If there is a numerically linear relationship between what is in the blood and the dose, such as the findings suggested in Mattsson et al. (2000), or those reported in Eaton et al. (2008), then a pregnant mother exposed at the aggregate exposure level estimated by EPA (i.e., 0.00067 mg/kg/day) may result in exposure to the fetus at a level of ~0.00067 µg/L, which is not likely to be detectable with typical detection limits of ~ 4 µg/L (Marty et al. 2007). So, even in vitro mechanistic studies designed to show an effect at very low levels are still using doses that are unlikely to be seen in fetal or even neonatal rats.

A preponderance of studies have now shown that chlorpyrifos, and a few other OP insecticides at doses 100 or more times higher than current EPA estimates of exposure, have mechanisms different than those causing acute or subchronic toxicity. Thus far, no studies have shown that these effects occur at the known environmental levels. The whole issue may soon become moot, as manufacturers are either not re-registering OP insecticides or EPA is further canceling their uses. Nevertheless, one could question whether any evidence supports neurobehavioral effects during the time that these types of insecticides were heavily used. Several neurological endpoints might be probed to answer this question. For example, one could look at trends in autism spectrum disorders or IQ in general as being related to exposure to neurotoxicants. Thus, one hypothesis would be that if chlorpyrifos were as potent as mechanistic lab studies are interpreted, then trend data would show a downward direction, especially when these compounds were most intensely used.

The present literature on autism spectrum disorders does not indicate that neurotoxicant pesticides like chlorpyrifos are etiologic factors in this disease phenomenon (e.g., Newschaffer et al. 2007). Furthermore, trend data indicates a rapid rise in diagnosed cases during the late 90s and early 2000s (Spzir 2006) at a time when OP insecticide use was declining.

Another curious observation relates to trends in IQ, which of course can be a controversial subject in itself, as discussions devolve into the classic nurture vs.

nature debate. Nevertheless, there has been a trend in rising IQs since the 1950s (Lynn and Pagliari 1994; Blair et al. 2005), a period when some of the first OP insecticides became commercially available. (Major intelligence improvements are seen in the domain of abstract problem-solving ability on cultural-free tests (Colom et al. 2005).) The phenomenon of rising IQs (know as the Flynn effect, after seminal research by Flynn 1984, 1987) in many countries worldwide may be slowing down in recent years (Teasdale and Owen 2008), but ironically the hypothesized recent trend seems coincident with severe restrictions on OP insecticide use and even outright cancellations of uses. Thus, if OP insecticides were potent enough to cause neurodevelopmental anomalies in association with levels of real-world exposures, one would predict both a direct correlation with use and trends in macro-level effects like autism and IQ. Yet such a correlation is not present, or is opposite what would be predicted.

Pyrethroid Insecticides

The term "pyrethroid" refers to all synthetic versions of insecticidal compounds based on the structure of components of the botanical extract called pyrethrum. *Chrysanthemum cinaerifolium,* one of about 30 species in the genus *Chrysanthemum,* is particularly useful as a source of pyrethrum extracts that become concentrated in the flowers. While gardeners still tell tales of planting chrysanthemums to ward off insect pests around their gardens, in fact only *C. cinaerifolium* is a useful source of pyrethrum, and it is not commercially produced in the U.S. This particular species is still cultivated commercially for its trove of pyrethrum components, but the geographic foci include Kenya, Rwanda, Ecuador, and Australia (Gullickson 1995; Wainaina 1995; Mac-Donald 1995). Pyrethrum and, more specifically, pyrethrins, which are components of the whole extract, are sold commercially, and are one of the few neurotoxic insecticides approved for certified organic agricultural production under the USDA National Organic Program and various State organic program rules (WSDA 2010).

Because the synthetic pyrethroids have generally the same mechanism of biochemical toxicity as the naturally occurring pyrethrins, consideration

Figure 12.

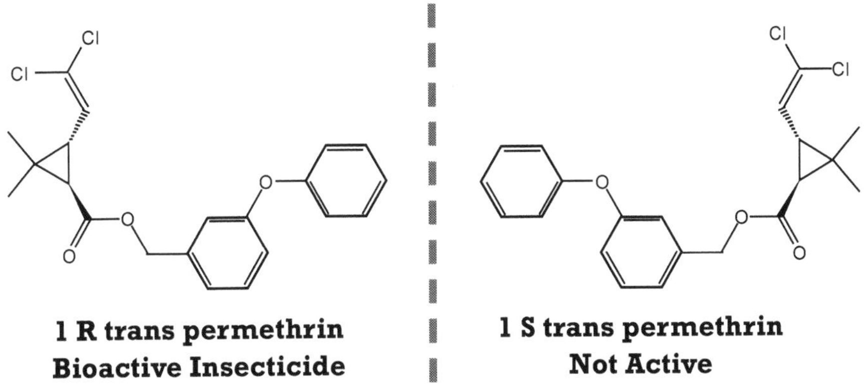

1 R trans permethrin
Bioactive Insecticide

1 S trans permethrin
Not Active

Pyrethrins and their synthetic analogs exist as enantiomeric mixtures that consist of identical molecules existing in two distinct three-dimensional configurations that are mirror images of each other, much like a left hand cannot be superimposed on a right hand. Such chemistry is significant from the perspective of biological activity, as noted above for the synthetic pyrethroid permethrin.

of the historical aspects of the invention of these compounds and their use helps elucidate the modern safety record of these compounds. Pyrethrum-containing flowers were likely first used as palliatives for warding off body and head lice in the early 1800s among tribes of the Caucasus region and in Persia (Casida 1980). Pyrethrins, and also permethrin—which is a synthetic analog of the natural products—have medicinal uses today to treat head lice infestations occasionally affecting young public school-age children. However, use of pyrethrins and pyrethroids in this manner is strictly under regulatory control of the Food and Drug Administration (FDA) rather than EPA.

Pyrethrum, a complex mixture of at least six bioactive components, is concentrated in *C. cinaerifolium* flowers. Each flower contains about 3-4 mg of pyrethrins, the most insecticidal components of the pyrethrum mixture (Casida 1980). Flowers were dried and traditionally applied to the body as a powder. In Japan during the early 1900s, the flowers were extracted and components partially elucidated (Katsuda 1999), with more definitive structural determinations made in Germany. In the 1920s, flowers were extracted commercially with kerosene to isolate and concentrate the active principal components (Casida 1980).

One important aspect of the early work on pyrethrum mixture chemistry was the discovery that the individual components consisted of a melange of three-dimensionally distinct structures called stereoisomers. Stereoisomers are molecules that share the same molecular formula and sequence of bonded atoms but are different in the three-dimensional spatial orientations of their atoms (Moss 1996). The pyrethrins and their synthetic derivatives, for example, are special types of stereoisomers called enantiomers because they exist in at least two different three-dimensional configurations that are mirror images of each other. Molecules that are mirror images are not superimposable, analogous to the right and left hand of an individual (Figure 12). Research has proven that enantiomers have different levels of toxicity and also rates of environmental degradation (Elliott and Janes 1977; Qin et al. 2008). Thus, to simply talk about potency of most pyrethrins and their synthetic derivatives is misleading because, in reality, they are enantiomeric mixtures, and not all the components are insecticidal. Nevertheless, elucidation of the complexity of three-dimensional structure gave impetus to the discovery of synthetic analogs that could potentially enhance insecticidal qualities of the natural product (Katsuda 1999). Such enhancements lead to more selective compounds that are more potent against pests and thus can be applied in comparatively lower amounts.

Pyrethrins can be rapid-acting and extraordinarily toxic to a number of insect pest species, yet of extraordinarily low toxicity to mammals. However, pyrethrins have little to no use in agriculture because they literally degrade in hours when exposed to sunlight (Elliott 1976). This environmental lability is arguably one rationale that the USDA National Organic Standards Board (NOSB), under recommendation of the Organic Materials Research Institute (OMRI), has used to approve natural toxins for use by certified organic farmers. Ironically, if a pest infestation is not controlled sufficiently by using the unstable pyrethrins, a farm manager may feel justified in making repeated applications, which of course requires more labor, more chemical cost, and increased fuel and water usage. Thus, the ideal would be to "invent" a compound with the safety (i.e., very low toxicity) of pyrethrins but with sufficient environmental longevity such that one application would typically be sufficiently effective, especially if a well thought-out IPM plan were deployed.

With goals of increasing biological activity and environmental persistence of the natural pyrethrum constituents, Michael Elliott and coworkers obtained funding from the British government to examine ways to alter the pyrethrin structure to increase environmental stability against sunlight without losing its safety with respect to birds and mammals. Tinkering with the structure, Elliott and his team were credited with inventing the first stable synthetic pyrethroids (Elliott et al. 1973a), as well as pyrethrin analogs with greater insecticidal activity but even lower vertebrate toxicity than the natural products (Elliott et al. 1973b). This research laid the groundwork for synthesis of many analogs, wherein tinkering with the basic pyrethrins structure increased persistence without substantially altering mammalian safety and high potency as an insecticide.

Closer examination of the reasons why pyrethrins and derivatives are safe for mammals and birds but not for insect pests is consistent with the themes of selectivity among species and the role of pharmacokinetics in predicting the likelihood of biological effect. Pyrethrins are quickly metabolized to nontoxic compounds by birds and mammals, and thus when exposed via the skin, as would be typical of environmental or medicinal use, these components are extraordinarily safe yet effective at killing insect pests. Part of the selectivity from environmental dermal exposures comes from very low penetrability (~1% in human skin) (Ray and and Forshaw 2000). In general, the synthetic derivatives, which have evolved in structure over the last 30 years, have similar properties of extraordinary safety and effectiveness. In addition to low potential for pyrethroids to cross the epidermis, selectivity among insects and mammals and birds is due to differences in the ability of pyrethroids to bind to vertebrate and insect nerve membranes, differences in metabolic pathways between mammals and insects, and the fact that insects are "cold-blooded" (Casida and Quistad 2004; Narahasi et al. 2007).

First, the natural pyrethrins and synthetic versions all bind to proteins in the nerve cell membranes along the signal conducting axon. These proteins act like gated channels, allowing the influx of sodium into the axon, but they only open and close briefly in response to an electrical stimulus (i.e., a voltage change across the membrane caused by an oncoming nerve signal). Pyrethroids bind to the protein, preventing it from closing quickly, causing a prolongation of nerve signaling (Narahashi 1987; Soderlund and Bloomquist 1989). However, vertebrate sodium channels have a very low binding affinity for pyrethroids, but the insect channel protein is bound very readily by extremely small quantities of pyrethroid. Thus, pyrethroids are typically hundreds to thousands of times less toxic to mammals than to insects (Elliott 1976; Casida et al. 1983; Katsuda 1999). Such differences mean that very small amounts of pyrethroids can be deployed to control insects, and these amounts are vastly lower than the amounts that might cause harm to mammals. Secondly, mammals can very rapidly detoxify pyrethroids with two types of enzyme systems (i.e., esteratic and oxidative enzymes), but insects cannot because they are deficient in esterases that are active against these chemicals.

A third reason for differential toxicity between insects and mammals is that toxicity of pyrethroids rises as temperature falls, a phenomenon not seen by other extant types of insecticides (Narahashi 2007). The highly protective role of the skin in preventing entry of toxic substances into the blood stream (i.e., systemic circulation) is illustrated in lab experiments wherein direct injection of natural pyrethrins into the blood results in lethality at doses quite similar to the most neurotoxically potent OP insecticides like the banned parathion. The continued approval of certain formulations of pyrethrins for use in organic agriculture (e.g., Long et al. 2005; Zehnder et al. 2007; Reganold 2010) leads to the conclusion that at least some advocates have realized how toxicity is greatly modified by pharmacokinetic phenomena.

The insecticidal activity of pyrethrins and certain older synthetic derivatives can be enhanced by an additive called piperonyl butoxide (PBO). Although formulations including PBO are not permissible for use in certified organic agriculture, many household versions of pyrethrins that are sold to consumers do contain PBO. PBO functions as a synergist that inhibits microsomal oxidase enzymes (Hodgson and Levi 1998), further reducing the ability of insects to detoxify the pyrethrins. Because humans can detoxify pyrethrins by a different metabolic pathway than do insects (i.e., via esterase cleavage (Abernathy and Casida 1973)), PBO is of very low concern for human health under permissible usage conditions. Interestingly, the toxicity of the modern pyrethroids is not enhanced sufficiently by PBO to warrant adding this synergist to their commercial formulations.

The historical record and knowledge of toxicological mechanisms accumulated over the last 50 years shows that use of a naturally occurring botanical component and its synthetic derivatives has a high degree of safety. So, what are the objections to using such technology? Aside from the general disdain for use of synthetic chemicals in agriculture (or other social sectors) among certain advocates, rumblings questioning the safety of these compounds have emerged over the last few years. Atypically, however, long-term concerns about cancer or neurodevelopment do not seem to be strong motivators for these concerns, as are those that have been observed for older chemistries. After all, the literature shows the pyrethroid structures are not mutagenic (Pluijmen et al. 1984; Miyamoto et al. 1995). Furthermore, the environmental use rates are at least 10-fold lower than the use rates for the older chemistries, and thus exposure potential is quite limited. Pyrethroids are used in commercial agriculture, but their use tends to be limited to field crops, including cotton and corn, and some vegetables rather than to fruit crops. Entomologists are wary of recommending pyrethroids in fruit crops, owing to their tendency to knock out beneficial predacious mites and thus stimulate a pest mite outbreak (Hoyt et al. 1978; Hull et al. 1985). Indeed, the judicious use of pyrethroids is evidenced by monitoring data that shows most fruit and vegetables do not have pyrethroid insecticide residues (USDA AMS 2009).

Perhaps the biggest factor in pushing newspaper stories that question pyrethrins, and thus pyrethroids safety, comes from the use of lice control shampoo formulations. As stated above, such use is considered pharmaceutical and under control of the FDA. Flames were fanned within the last several years over an advocacy report that questioned whether pyrethroid chemistries were actually as safe as advertised (Pell and Morris 2008). Recent reassessments of safety, leading to re-registration of the pesticides, delineated the overall low acute and chronic toxicity of these compounds (EPA 2006), but such documentation was ignored in favor of a database of complaints from people using pyrethroids at home for lice control. The advocacy report led off with a story about a child who died following the parents' use of a pyrethrin product to rid her of head lice. However, the report did not question whether the product was used strictly as directed, which is expected of consumers using any type of medication. Indeed, the report mentioned the child being in the bathtub while her parents washed down her hair, but it did not connect the two events. In fact, product labels strictly tell parents to apply the insecticidal shampoo dry by rubbing directly into the scalp and then washing off after a short contact time (Frankowski et al. 2002). The label informs parents the product should not be administered in the bath, which would easily cause the active ingredient to penetrate highly penetrable body regions such as the genitalia. Head lice products may be applied one more time within 7-10 days after the first application. When this stricture is violated, transient toxicity could result—as was reported for a toddler whose parents applied a pyrethrin product three times within a 12-day period (Hammond and Leikin 2008).

Reports to poison centers following use of pyrethrin-type products has a long history, partly because these products have been on the market a long time. But most reports involve some kind of skin sensitivity or irritation. Such observations are especially true with pyrethrum extracts for two reasons. First, because the extracts are derived from flower parts, allergic reactions are possible. Indeed, head lice shampoo products warn against use if allergy to ragweed is suspected, although modern extraction techniques minimize the co-extraction of allergens (Frankowski et al. 2002). Second, natural pyrethrin extracts have long been known to cause a skin tingling and burning sensation called parasthesia (Ray and Forshaw 2000). However, the sensations associated with parasthesia are temporary effects that are incidental to the specific neurotoxicological effects of the insecticides known from insect and rodent studies.

A second recent issue seems to be restricted to California, where pyrethroid insecticides are heavily used in urban environments. Extensive monitoring studies of urban streams have shown the presence of multiple types of pyrethroid insecticides in the bottom sediments. Pyrethroid residues will bind very tightly to sediments, limiting bioavailability to species like fish swimming in the water column (You et al. 2008). Indeed, very few, if any, residues can be measured in water because the water solubility of most pyrethroids is extremely low. Bioassays with sediments collected from urban waterways in California have been tested using *Hyalella azteca*, a sediment-dwelling amphipod. A positive correlation has been reported with increasing detections of multiple pyrethroid insecticide residues and lethality of the sediments to the amphipod (Weston et al. 2005; Amweg et al. 2006). However, a clear NO-AEC is present in the dataset. Furthermore, similar monitoring in Tennessee, another State where pyrethroid use in urban areas is likely prevalent, showed few pyrethroid detections in the sediment and no toxicity to amphipods (Amweg et al. 2006). These observations suggest that urbanites in California may be disproportionately disposing of pyrethroid rinse water on hard surfaces following lawn and house pest control, thereby increasing the chance of direct runoff into sewage drains. Further studies should elucidate pathways of contamination and suggest improved educational programs for homeowner disposal of pesticide waste.

Now that OP insecticide use has decreased significantly in agriculture and been practically eliminated from urban use, pyrethroid insecticides have become the dominant insecticides, especially in residential areas. Thus, increasing focus on sublethal effects will be seen in the literature, and claims of low dose effects are likely to be made, somewhat similarly to those claimed for the effects of chlorpyrifos on neurodevelopment. Indeed, some studies have shown that pyrethroid insecticides can interact with the estrogen or androgen receptors (Du et al. 2010). However, the flaw in assessing hazard, let alone risk, from this new crop of studies remains the same. The premise that the studies represent low-dose exposures is not consistent with exposure estimates. Furthermore, *in vitro* studies use doses that are orders of magnitude higher than estimates of pyrethroid residues in blood, which could be considered a surrogate for understanding concentration effects at the cellular level. Also, *in vitro* studies tend to use dimethyl sulfoxide to dissolve the hydrophobic pyrethroid insecticides, thereby creating an artificially high bioavailability that does not occur in living organisms.

An example of ignoring how concentration is related to effects is illustrated in perhaps the first study to suggest that pyrethroids have endocrine receptor binding activity in cultures with estrogen responsive cell lines (Garey et al. 1998). Examination of the graphs in this report suggests that binding may have occurred with doses of fenvalerate around 420 µg/L (~1 µM). To place this concentration in perspective, examination of blood levels of pyrethroids is useful. One study of blood samples from 45 human volunteers who had been exposed nightly to repellent uses of pyrethroids for mosquito control found no pyrethroid residues were detected at a limit of 0.5 µg/L(Ramesh and Ravi 2004). This fenvalerate detection limit is 800 times lower than the levels causing a positive response *in vitro* . To place the lack of potency of fenvalerate in perspective, let alone the high dose tested relative to blood levels (or lack thereof), estrogen (i.e., estradiol) gave a similar cell response as fenvalerate at a concentration of ~0.006 µg/L (Garey et al. 1998). Thus, in the cell culture assay, estradiol is about 70,000 times more potent than fenvalerate. A baseline estradiol level in the blood of human males is ~0.028 µg/L (Raven et al. 2006). Thus, normal males have about five times as much estradiol in their blood as has been proven to cause an *in vitro* response in estrogen-responsive cells. Yet, after chronic environmental exposures, males have no detectable levels of fenvalerate, suggesting that concerns about endocrine system effects are unwarranted if one considers that natural titers of estrogen themselves are far more potent than fenvalerate. Other studies that show an estrogenic response from pyrethroid exposures *in vitro* suffer the same logical flaw of conflating concentrations used in the laboratory with actual environmental exposures. Furthermore, such studies ignore the titers of the highly potent natural hormone estradiol.

Glyphosate

Glyphosate-containing formulations have been marketed since about 1975. Glyphosate itself is best chemically described as a phosphonated amino acid. In fact, part of the structure is actually glycine, a natural, non-essential amino acid. The only known primary mechanism of biochemical toxicity of glyphosate at the rates of use as a herbicide is through inhibition of the EPSPS enzyme

(Schonbrunn et al. 1991; Sikorski and Gruys 1997). This enzyme is specific to plant metabolism, although it also occurs in some bacteria. Specifically, plants synthesize aromatic amino acids in the shikimic acid pathway that involves EPSPS. Animals, lacking the pathway, must acquire these types of compounds from their diet. For this reason, any environmental residues resulting from legal uses of glyphosate-containing formulations are often orders of magnitude lower than doses causing lethality to aquatic or terrestrial organisms. The World Health Organization (WHO 2005), the Environmental Protection Agency (EPA 1993), and the European Union (EC 2002) have extensively reviewed the full range of toxicological information about glyphosate, pronouncing it of extremely low toxicity and thus near-zero risk. In addition to scrutiny by the various regulatory agencies, numerous risk assessments have been published in the scholarly literature (for example, Geisy et al. 2000; Williams et al. 2000; Solomon et al. 2007). These latter publications pertinently consider all the toxicological endpoints that have been defined, including both the regulatory and mechanistic toxicology data, and integrate the most sensitive effects with the likely exposures. None have suggested any environmental or human health hazard from routine legally sanctioned uses of glyphosate.

Glyphosate has broad spectrum activity against most plants, and thus it historically had very limited uses in growing agricultural crops. Furthermore, only young weeds are susceptible to glyphosate at the levels that are allowed for use. Once weeds grow and develop extensive root systems, glyphosate is much less effective at complete control and thus does not hold any greater potency than other less broad-spectrum herbicides. With the advent of soybeans, corn, and cotton in the U.S. bred using biotechnological techniques involving a resistant bacterial EPSPS gene or a modified resistant plant EPSPS gene, glyphosate in the mid 1990s began to be used widely on these field crops. Today, glyphosate-containing formulations are the most widely used herbicides, ostensibly owing to the disproportionately large acreages of the three aforementioned crops (USDA NASS 2009). As would be predicted from environmental chemistry models, the greater volumes of glyphosate used would lead to detections of residues in water and occasionally in unprocessed soybeans or corn. However, despite the vast acreages treated, fewer than one-third of monitored water samples have detectable levels of glyphosate, and the concentrations are typically less than 1 μg/L (Battaglin et al. 2005).

For glyphosate to be optimally effective against plants, it is applied in conjunction with a surfactant. Thus far, Monsanto, the original patent holder and still the main manufacturer of glyphosate products, continues to formulate glyphosate in formulations that contain the surfactant POEA. Various versions of the formulation called Roundup are typically the most prevalently used form of glyphosate in the U.S. This polyethoxytallowamine surfactant seems to best facilitate the penetration of glyphosate through leaf surfaces. Of all the herbicides in the market today, the presence of POEA has created the most confusion regarding the question of glyphosate toxicity versus its formulations toxicity. POEA is a comparatively potent surfactant and, given the well-known mechanism of surfactant interactions with cell membranes (Bonsall and Hunt 1971; Jones 1999), its presence in formulations of glyphosate are predictably more toxic to aquatic organisms than glyphosate alone. However, the amounts of POEA in any glyphosate formulation are approximately three times lower than the concentrations of glyphosate itself. Furthermore, POEA rapidly degrades in the presence of sediment if it should run off or drift into water (Wang et al. 2005).

Because of the general mistrust in Europe of crops bred using genetic modification, such as the Roundup Ready crops, glyphosate-containing herbicides have been the focus of intense scrutiny by environmental advocates. Thus, in addition to raising doubts about the safety of the crops themselves, despite the plethora of scholarly papers proving a lack of adverse effects, environmental advocacy groups have highlighted two areas of research that stem from one specific laboratory in the U.S. and two laboratories in Europe. The published papers from these labs are discussed to illustrate why regulatory agencies still consider glyphosate to be of essentially zero risk for all approved uses.

First, on the heels of concerns about the effect of low aquatic concentrations of atrazine on the African leopard frog, reports from a U.S. lab suggested adverse effects of Roundup on several different frog species (see Relyea 2005a,b,c,d). While the press releases based on lab research stir up strong feelings, they do not focus on the critical aspect of these studies that make them irrelevant to assessing whether the actual agricultural use of glyphosate can harm frog populations. Specifically, the concentrations in water that putatively cause frog lethality in the aforementioned published experiments are at least an order of magnitude higher than what is found in the environment, even after an overspray (Battaglin et al. 2009; Goldsborough and Beck 1989; Goldsborough and Brown 1993; Newton et al. 1984; Scribner et al. 2007, Tsui and Chan 2008). Although an overspray of a Roundup formulation across a body of water is expressly prohibited by the product label, glyphosate itself rapidly dissipates in water within 24 hours. Under laboratory conditions representing direct application of Roundup to water, toxicity to the subject frog species was detected only following 10 days of exposure. Thus, the extrapolation of observations from a lab study to the environment is not supported by simply examining known concentrations. Furthermore, even when caged frogs were tested during actual commercial applications, no unusual adverse effects were noted, either following exposure to expected environmental concentrations (Wojtaszek et al. 2004) or residues resulting from commercial forestry spray operations (Thompson et al. 2004). A deterministic and probabilistic risk assessment applied to direct oversprays of glyphosate-containing herbicides also concluded little impact on a diversity of aquatic species (Solomon and Thompson 2003).

The second set of studies from two laboratories in Europe has been interpreted to find that sub-agricultural use rates of glyphosate can cause cytotoxicity in various types of cells (e.g., Marc et al. 2002; Benachour and Seralini 2009). Pertinently, the data from these studies strongly suggest that the toxicity is more likely due to the surfactant POEA in the Roundup formulations than due to the glyphosate active ingredient itself. The problem with these studies, however, is that the levels of exposure (i.e., body dose) from using Roundup formulations mixed in a spray tank are many orders of magnitude lower than the concentration in the spray tank. The authors of the European studies have mistakenly interpreted their data as representing what workers and perhaps the general public are exposed to. The subject studies have all been *in vitro* examinations of cell cultures and/or enzyme systems exposed to either Roundup formulations or glyphosate. The authors of those studies end their papers by concluding that the 10-1000 ppm of Roundup equivalents that the cells are exposed to represent actual human worker exposures. In none of the papers have the authors attempted to use any of the pharmacokinetic data from controlled exposure of rodents or any of the clinical literature to examine whether their cell exposure levels make sense from an environmental perspective. For example, in one of the latest papers (Benachour and Seralini 2009), the authors begin to see some cellular toxicity in a cell culture exposed to one Roundup formulation with a glyphosate dose equivalent to 20 µg/mL. While this concentration seems low to the authors, in reality it is equivalent to a blood level exposure about five times higher than that measured in the blood of rodents after an extreme exposure to an oral dose of 400 mg/kg glyphosate in corn oil, a notably effective solvent at facilitating toxicant or drug absorption (Anadon et al. 2009). To put this dose in perspective, the worst case exposure to an adult female pesticide applicator from all possible exposure routes has been estimated at ~0.125 mg/kg, or 3200 times less than the exposure given to test rodents. Yet, the authors of the cytotoxicity studies failed to critically analyze their data in comparison to the 4.6 µg/mL level in blood following the extreme rodent exposure. Furthermore, the authors ignored the fact that skin exposure only results in about 3% absorption of glyphosate in a 24-hour period, and absorption from the intestine is less than 40%.

In summary, pronouncements of adverse effects of glyphosate and its surfactant seem relegated solely to the laboratory; in the environment, exposure is just too low for any measurable effects. Indeed, the European authors own studies show clear thresholds for an effect. In other words, their studies show that, at some concentrations in the cell cultures, nothing happens. Proclaiming that spray tank concentrations of glyphosate expose workers to hazardous levels of glyphosate and its surfactants defies logic in the light of actual exposure measurements and *in vivo* rodent studies. The interpretation of *in vitro* studies is realistic only when concentrations reflect levels likely to occur in blood and/or interstitial fluids.

Conclusions

In the new world of 24/7 information demands, we seemingly have more headlines with less informational content. In the world of toxicology, basic research dominates all published subjects, and thus just about any chemical ever studied is perceived as having an adverse effect. These studies that overwhelmingly are mechanistic in focus become the fodder for the 24/7 info-news culture. On the other hand, the risk assessment reports that EPA issues with each pesticide registration decision, or the infrequently published but still accessible regulatory toxicology research papers are not very interesting to a society hooked on the adrenaline rush of a disaster movie. Perhaps this pronouncement is harsh about our modern perspectives, but an honest assessment of the wide array of pesticide studies and application of the risk assessment paradigm does not support the perspective of widespread adverse health effects, or even ecological effects, from modern pesticide use. Indeed, in the four cases highlighted within this report, so-called low dose effects are not really caused by low doses when one examines the actual exposures.

Furthermore, in some cases, as is true for atrazine, one set of studies is directly refuted by another set of studies. Certainly, all studies should be subjected to vigorous debate, as science should endeavor to make happen. But in a press release world of communication, only the truly scary stories get told.

Some advocates have been pressing the idea that the paradigm for toxicological phenomena has shifted over the last fifteen years from a focus on cancer to a focus on endocrine system effects. Some advocates argue that current pesticide regulations fail to keep up with modern techniques for examining hormonally active agents. But upon close examination to determine what is missing, one finds a plethora of *in vitro* testing that overestimates by large amounts what is expected in a whole person's blood, bolus exposures that defy the reality of environmental exposures, and measuring of tissues without definition of what it means to the whole organism. To claim that industry has not been testing for endocrine system effects is to ignore the value of whole organism developmental and multigenerational reproductive toxicity tests mandated for many years by EPA (Stevens et al. 1997). The system of testing has not been static, as EPA has incorporated new measurable endpoints.

Another paradigm being pushed involves the idea that organisms are exposed to multiple residues of contaminants. The response to such a paradigm shifter is, frankly, yes. When an organism eats any food, but especially plants, they are exposed to multiple highly bioactive biochemicals, a number of which have known "toxicological" effects when tested at sufficient doses, just like all other xenobiotic chemicals. So, nothing seems new here. Indeed, counter-analysis suggests that concerns about pesticide mixtures are overblown because the environmental levels of exposure are just too low to have measurable effects (Carpy et al. 2000).

Missing from much of the public debate are the benefits of chemical technology, especially as applied to crop protection. Negative critiques of modern agriculture are vaguely familiar as echoes of complaints nearly 40 years ago, just prior to the suspension by EPA of DDT use for agriculture. The report herein did not engage in trying to defend old chemical technology because agriculture has moved far beyond it. Crop protection specialists themselves began long ago to argue for the judicious use of crop protection agents. Industry long ago began to examine the problems of the most persistent chemicals with broad spectrums of toxicity to nontarget organisms and synthesize new compounds with less persistence, less toxicity, and greater selectivity for specific pests versus nontarget organisms. Furthermore, the amounts of new chemicals needed to control pests today are small fractions of what they were just 20 years ago.

Some advocates call for wholesale adoption of organic agriculture. But if the calls are motivated by concerns about pesticide use, then disappointment will reign because USDA rules for certification of organic agriculture do allow pesticide use. But it is a "pick your poison" choice of eschewing certain products in favor of others. Ironically, some of the same active ingredients with known nervous system toxicity used by so-called conventional growers are also used by practitioners of organic agriculture.

Finally, we in the United States take for granted our country's lack of serious outbreaks of epidemic disease transmitted by insect vectors. We ignore the fact of 300 million new cases of malaria elsewhere each year and the devastating effects on an economy. The list of vectored diseases is large, but we do not think about the important contributions of pesticide use to the protection of our public health. Yet communities besieged by outbreaks of biting mosquitoes clamor for their communities to be treated with mosquito control insecticides, as long as it is done out of sight at night. Studies have proven that bans of DDT in South America were correlated with increased incidences of malaria that plummeted when spraying of wall surfaces resumed. If one doesn't like DDT, one still cannot ignore the effectiveness of pyrethroid-treated bed nets to protect sleeping kids and their parents from feeding mosquitoes. Indeed, such nets, which would cost us the equivalent of pennies, are expensive commodities to many in the world.

The point is, chemical technology has improved, and will continue to improve, human health, whether helping to make vegetables and fruits of high quality more abundant and cheaper or to preserve the health of individuals who can then help their society to progress.

References

Abernathy CO, Casida JE. 1973. Pyrethroid insecticides: Esterase cleavage in relation to selective toxicity. Science 179: 1235-1236.

Acquavella J, Olsen G., Cole P, Ireland B, Kaneene J, Schuman S, Holden L. 1998. Cancer among farmers: A meta-analysis. Ann Epidemiol 8: 64-74.

Aldridge JE, Levin ED, Seidler FJ, Slotkin TA. 2005a. Developmental exposure of rats to chlorpyrifos leads to behavioral alterations in adulthood, involving serotonergic mechanisms and resembling animal models of depression. Environmental Health Perspectives 113(5): 527-531.

Aldridge JE, Meyer AS, Seidler FJ, Slotkin TA. 2005b. Alternations in central nervous system serotenergic and dopaminergic synaptic activity in adulthood after prenatal or neonatal chlorpyrifos exposure. Environ Health Perspect 113(8): 1027-1031.

Ames BN, Gold LW. 1997. Environmental pollution, pesticides, and the prevention of cancer: Misconceptions. FASEB J 11: 1041-1052.

Ames BN, Profet M, Gold LS. 1990a. Dietary pesticides (99.99 percent all natural). Proc Natl Acad Sci 87(19): 7777-7781.

Ames, BN, Profet, M, and Gold, LS. 1990b Nature's chemicals and synthetic chemicals: Comparative toxicology. Proc. Natl. Acad. Sci. USA 87, 7782-7786

References

Amweg EL, Weston DP, You J, Lydy MJ. 2006. Pyrethroid insecticides and sediment toxicity in urban creeks from California and Tennessee. Environ Sci Technol 40(5): 1700-1706.

Anadon A, Martinez-Larranaga MR, Martinez MA, Castellano VJ, Martinez M, Martin MT, et al. 2009. Toxicokinetics of glyphosate and its metabolite aminomethyl phosphonic acid in rats. Toxicology Letters 190: 91-95.

Artsob H, Gubler DJ, Enria DA, Morales MA, Pupo M, Bunning ML, et al. 2009. West Nile Virus in the New World: Trends in the spread and proliferation of West Nile virus in the Western hemisphere. Zoonoses Public Health 56: 357-369.

Bacon RM, Kugeler KJ, Mead PS. 2008. Surveillance for Lyme disease—-United States, 1992-2006. Morbidity & Mortality Weekly Report 57(SS10): 1-9. Available from: (http://www.cdc.gov/mmwr/preview/mmwrhtml/ss5710a1. htm)

Bakan B, Melcion D, Richard-Molard D, Cahagnier B. 2002. Fungal growth and Fusarium mycotoxin content in isogenic traditional maize and genetically modified maize grown in France and Spain. J Agric and Food Chem 50: 728-731.

Baker BP, Benbrook CM, Groth III E, Benbrook KL. 2002. Pesticide residues in conventional, integrated pest management (IPM)-grown and organic foods: insights from three US data sets. Food Additives and Contaminants 19(5): 427-446.

Barber LM, Schleier JJI, Peterson RKD. 2010. Economic cost analysis of West Nile virus outbreak, Sacramento County, California, USA, 2005. Emerging Infectious Diseases 16(3): 480-486.

Barlow F, Hadaway AB. 1956. Effect of changes in humidity on the toxicity and distribution of insecticides absorbed by some dried soils. Nature 178: 1299-1300.

Barringer F. 2008. Hermaphrodite frogs found in suburban ponds. NY Times (April 4, 2008): Available from: http://www.nytimes.com/2008/2004/2008/science/2008frog.html?_r=2005&oref=slogin&oref=slogin&oref=slogin.

Battaglin W, Rice KC, Focazio MJ, Salmons S, Barry RX. 2009. The occurrence of glyphosate, atrazine, and other pesticides in vernal pools and adjacent streams in Washington, DC, Maryland, Iowa, and Wyoming, 2005-2006. Environ Monitor Assess 155: 281-307.

Battaglin WA, Kolpin DW, Scribner EA, Kuivila KM, Sandstrom MW. 2005. Glyphosate, other herbicides, and transformation products in Midwestern streams, 2002. J Am Water Resources Association 41(2): 323-332.

Benachour N, Seralini G-E. 2009. Glyphosate formulations induce apoptosis and necrosis in human umbilical, embryonic, and placental cells. Chemical Research in Toxicology 22(1): 97-105.

Bonsall RW, Hunt S. 1971. Characteristics of interactions between surfactants and the human erythrocyte membrane. Biochimica et Biophysica Acta (BBA) - Biomembranes 249(1): 266-280.

Blair C, Gamson D, Thorne S, Baker DB. 2005. Rising mean IQ: Cognitive demand of mathematics education for young children, population exposure to formal schooling, and the neurobiology of the prefrontal cortex. Intelligence 33: 93-106.

Burney JA, Davis SJ, Lobell DB. 2010. Greenhouse gas mitigation by agricultural intensification. Proc Natl Acad Sci 107(26): 12052-12057.

Campbell CG, Seidler FJ, Slotkin TA. 1997. Chlorpyrifos interferes with cell development in rat brain regions. Brain Research Bulletin 43(2): 179-189.

Carney RM, Husted S, Jean C, Glaser C, Kramer V. 2008. Efficacy of aerial spraying of mosquito adulticide in reducing incidence of West Nile virus, California, 2005. Emerging Infectious Diseases 14(5): 747-754.

Carpenter, J.; Felsot, A; Goode, T.; Hammig, M.; Onstad, D.; Sankula, S. 2002. Comparative Environmental Impacts of Biotechnology-Derived and Traditional Soybean, Corn, and Cotton Crops. Council for Agricultural Science and Technology: Ames, IA. Available from: http://www.cast-science.org/biotechnology/index.html#biotechcropsbenefit

Carpy SA, Kobel W, Doe J. 2000. Health risk of low-dose pesticides mixtures: A review of the 1985-1998 literature on combination toxicology and health risk assessment. J Toxicol Environ Health Pt B 3: 1-25.

Carr JA, Gentles A, Smith EE, Goleman WL, Urquidi LJ, Thuett K, et al. 2003. Response of larval Xenopus laevis to agtrazine: assessment of growth, metamorphosis, and gonadal and laryngeal morphology. Environmental Toxicology and Chemistry: Vol 22, No 2, pp 396–405.

Casida JE, Gammon DW, and L. O. Ruzo., Glickman AH, Lawrence LJ. 1983. Mechanisms of selective action of pyrethroid insecticides. Ann Rev Pharmacol Toxicol 23: 413-438.

Casida JE, Quistad GB. 2004. Why insecticides are more toxic to insects than people: The unique toxicology of insects. J Pesticide Science 29: 81-86.

Casida JE. 1980. Pyrethrum flowers and pyrethoid insecticides. Environmental Health Perspectives 34: 189-202.

CFR (Code of Federal Regulations). 1997. Title 40: Protection of the Environment, Subpart D-REporting Requirements for Risk/Benefit Information. Available from: http://ecfrgpoaccessgov/cgi/t/text/text-idx?c=ecfr&sid=79ec7a10bc81 ccef6b4e48d34d856509&tpl=/ecfrbrowse/Title40/40cfr159_main_02tpl.

Chipman H, Kendall P, Auld G, Slater M, Keefe T. 1995. Consumer reaction to a risk/beneft/option message about agricultural chemicals in the food supply. Journal of Consumer Affairs 29(1): 144-163.

Coady KK, Murphy MB, Villeneuve DL, Hecker M, Jones PD, Carr JA, et al. 2005. Effects of atrazine on metamorphosis, growth, laryngeal and gonadal development, aromatase activity, and sex steroid concentrations in Xenopus laevis. Ecotoxicology Environmental Safety 62(2): 160-1733.

Coady KK, Murphy MG, Villeneuve DL, Hecker M, Jones PD, Carr JA, et al. 2004. Effects of atrazine on metamorphosis, growth, and gonadal development in the green frog (Rana clamitans). J Toxicol Environ Health, Pt A 67: 941-957.

Cohen N. 1997. The politics of environmental risk: Perceptions of risk assessment in the state legislatures. Policy Studies Journal 25(3): 470-484.

Collins A, Nasir A. 2010. Topical botulinum toxin. J Clin Aesthetic Dermatol 3(3): 35-39.

Colom R, Lluis-font JM, Andres-Pueyo A. 2005. The generational intelligence gains are caused by decreasing variance in the lower half of the distribution: supporting evidence for the nutrutition hypothesis. Intelligence 33: 83-91.

Cooper J, Dobson H. 2007. The benefits of pesticides to mankind and the environment. Crop Protection 26(9): 1337-1348.

Dam K, Garcia SJ, Seidler FJ, Slotkin TA. 1999. Neonatal chlorpyrifos exposure alters synaptic development and neuronal activity in cholinergic and catecholaminergic pathways. Developmental Brain Research 116: 9-20.

Dam K, Seidler FJ, Slotkin TA. 1998. Developmental neurotoxicity of chlorpyrifos: delayed targeting of DNA synthesis after repeated administration. Developmental Brain Research 108: 39-45.

Davis RS, Peterson RK, Macedo PA. 2007. An ecological risk assessment for insecticides used in adult mosquito management. Integrated Environmental Assessment and Management 3(3): 373-382.

Devine M, Duke SO, Fedtke C. 1993. Physiology of Herbicide Action (book). PTR Prentice Hall, Englewood Cliffs, New Jersey: 441 pp.

Dobzhansky T. 1964. Biology, molecular and organismic. American Zoologist 4(4): 443-452.

Du G, Shen O, Sun H, Fei J, Lu C, Song L, et al. 2010. Assessing hormone receptor activities of pyrethroid insecticides and their metabolites in reporter gene assays. Toxicological Sciences 116(1): 58-66.

Du Preez LH, Kunene N, Everson GJ, Carr JA, Giesy JP, Gross TS, et al. 2008. Reproduction, larval growth, and reproductive development in African clawed frogs (Xenopus laevis) exposed to atrazine. Chemosphere 71: 546-552.

Du Preez LH, Kunene N, Hanner R, Giesy JP, Solomon KR, Hosmer A, et al. 2009. Population-specific incidence of testicular ovarian follicles in Xenopus laevis from South Africa: A potential issue in endocrine testing. Aquatic Toxicology 95: 10-16.

Du Preez LH, Solomon Kr, Carr JA, Giesy JP, Gross Ts, Kendall RJ, et al. 2005. Population structure of the African clawed frog (Xenopus laevis) in maize-growing areas with atrazine application versus non-maize-growing area in South Africa. African Journal of Herpetology 54(1): 61-68.

Eaton DL, Daroff RB, Autrup H, Bridges JS, Buffler P, Costa LG, et al. 2008. Review of the toxicology of chlorpyrifos with an emphasis on human exposure and neurodevelopment. Critical Review in Toxicology S2: 1-125.

Elliott M, Farnham AW, Janes NF, Needham PH, Pulman DA, Stevenson JH. 1973a. A photostable pyrethroid. Nature 246: 169-170.

Elliott M, Farnham AW, Janes NF, Needham PH, Pulman DA. 1973b. Potent pyrethroid insecticides from modified cyclopropane acids. Nature 244: 456-457.

Elliott M, and Janes NF. 1977. Preferred conformations of pyrethroids. Synthetic Pyrethroids, Elliott, M (Ed); ACS Symposium Series 42: 29-36.

Elliott M. 1976. Properties and applications of pyrethroids. Environmental Health Perspectives 14: 3-13.

EPA (U.S. Environmental Protection Agency). 2002a. Atrazine: Toxicology Chapter of the Reregistration Eligibility Decision. SECOND REVISION. Memorandum TXR NO 0050644. Available from: http://www.epa.gov/opp00001/reregistration/atrazine/

EPA. 2002b. ATRAZINE/DACT - Fourth Report of the Hazard Identification Assessment Review Committee. Memorandum TXR NO 0050592. Available from: (http://www.epa.gov/opp00001/reregistration/atrazine/)

EPA. 1993. Voluntary reduced-risk initiative. Pesticide Regulation Notice 93-9.

EPA Office of Chemical Safety and Pollution Prevention. 2010. Harmonized Test Guidelines Available from: http://www.epa.gov/ocspp/pubs/frs/home/guidelin.htm

EPA. 1993. Reregistration Eligibility Decision Document. Glyphosate, List A, Case 0178. EPA 738-R-93-014 Office of Prevention, Pesticides, and Toxic Substances, USEPA, Washington, DC: Available from: http://www.epa.gov/REDs/.

EPA. 2000. Human health risk assessment-chlorpyrifos. US Environmental Protection Agency, Office of Pesticide Programs, Health Effects Division (7509C). Available from: http://www.epa.gov/opp00001/reregistration/chlorpyrifos/

EPA. 2002c. Reregistration eligibility science chapter for atrazine; Environmental fate and effects chapter. Available from: http://www.thecre.com/pdf/exhibit-a-efed_redchap_22apr02.pdf

EPA. 2006a. Reregistration Eligibility Decision for Chlorpyrifos. Available from: http://wwwepagov/opp00001/reregistration/chlorpyrifos/.

EPA. 2006. Reregistration eligibility decision for pyrethrins, cypermethrin, permethrin, resmethrin. Office of Pesticide Programs. Available from: http://www.epa.gov/pesticides/reregistration/status.htm.

EPA. 2010. What are biopesticides? Available from: http://www.epa.gov/oppb-ppd1/biopesticides/whatarebiopesticides.htm

EPA. 2011. Atrazine updates. Available from: http://www.epa.gov/oppsrrd1/reregistration/atrazine/atrazine_update.htm

European Commission. 2002. Review report for the active substance glyphosate. Commission Working Document 6511/VI/99-final.

Food & Drug Administration (FDA). 2009. Pesticide Monitoring Program FY 2007. Residue Monitoring Reports; FDA Pesticide Program Residue Monitoring: 1993-2007. Available from: http://www.fda.gov/Food/FoodSafety/FoodContaminantsAdulteration/Pesticides/ResidueMonitoringReports/ucm169577.htm.

Felsot, A. S. 1998. Numbers, numbers everywhere—and not a drop of meaning. J. Environmental Law and Litigation 13:91-113.

Felsot AS. 2010. Communicating safe pesticide use. Haye's Handbook of Pesticide Toxicology. Krieger, R I (Ed), Elsevier, New York: 1173-1187.

Felsot, A. S., and K. D. Racke. 2007. Chemical pest control technology: Benefits, disadvantages, and continuing roles in crop production systems. In Crop Protection Products for Organic Agriculture. Environmental, Health, and Efficacy Assessment. Felsot, A.S., K. D. Racke (ed.); American Chemical Society Symposium Series 947, Am. Chem. Soc., Washington, DC. pp. 1-18.

Fernandez-Cornejo J, Jans S, Smith M. 1998. Issues in the economics of pesticide use in agriculture: A review of the empirical evidence. Review of Agricultural Economics 20(2): 462-488.

Flynn JR. 1984. The mean IQ of Americans: Massive gains 1932 to 1978. Psychological Bulletin 95(1): 29-51.

Flynn, J. (1987). Massive IQ gains in 14 nations: What IQ tests really measure. Psychological Bulletin, 101(2), 171–191

Frankowski BL, Weiner LB, et al. 2002. Head lice. Pediatrics 110: 638-643.

Gaido K, Dohme L, Wang F, Chen I, Blankvoort B, Ramamoorthy K, et al. 1998. Comparative estrogenic activity of wine extracts and organochlorine pesticide residues in food. Envirin Health perspect 106(Supplement 6): 1347-1351.

Gammon DW, Aldous CN, Carr WCJ, Sanborn JR, Pfeifer Kf. 2005. A risk assessment of atrazine use in California: Human health and ecological aspects. Pest Magement Science 61: 331-355.

Garey J, Wolff MS. 1998. Estrogenic and antiprogestagenic activities of pyrethroid insecticides. Biochemical and Biophysical Research Communications 251: 855-859.

Gianessi LP, Reigner NP. 2006. The value of herbicides in U.S. crop production. 2005 Update. Crop Protection Research Institute, CropLife Foundation, Washington, DC. Available from:: http://www.croplifefoundation.org/cpri_benefits_herbicides.htm.

Gianessi LP, Reigner NP. 2007. The value of herbicides in U.S. crop production. Weed Technology 21: 559-566.

Giesy JP, Dobson S, Solomon KR. 2000. Ecotoxicological risk assessment for Roundup herbicide. Reviews of Environmental Contamination and Toxicology 167: 35-120.

Goldsborough LG, Beck AE. 1989. Rapid dissipation of glyphosate in small forest ponds. Arch Environ Contam Toxicol 18: 537-544.

Goldsborough LG, Brown DJ. 1993. Dissipation of glyphosate and aminomethylphosphonic acid in water and sediments of boreal forest ponds. Environmental Toxicology and Chemistry 12: 1139-1147.

Gribble GW. 1998. Naturally occurring organohalogen compounds. Accounts of Chemical Research 31: 141-152.

Gullickson WD, Sr. 1995. History of pyrethrum in the1970s and 1980s. Pyrethrum Flowers Production, Chemistry, Toxicology, and Uses. Casida, J E and Quistad, G B (Eds) Oxford University Press, New York. 32-46.

References

Hammond K, Leikin JB. 2008. Topical pyrethrin toxicity leading to acute-onset stuttering in a toddler. American Journal of Therapeutics 15: 323-324.

Hansen JA, Holm L, Frewer L, Robinson P, Sandoe P. 2003. Beyond the knowledge deficit: recent research into lay and expert attitudes to food risks. Appetite 41: 111-121.

Haseman JK, Bailer AJ, Kodell RL, Morris R, Portier K. 2001. Statistical issues in the analysis of low-dose endocrine disruptor data. Toxicological Sciences 61: 201-210.

Hayes WJ. 1991. Handbook of pesticides toxicology. General Principles. Vol. 1 Academic Press, San Diego, CA.

Hayes T, Haston K, Tsui MTK, Hoang A, Haeffele C, Vonk A. 2003. Atrazine-induced hermaphroditism at 0.1 ppb in American leopard frogs (Rana pipiens): Laboratory and field evidence. Environ Health Persp 111: 568-575.

Hayes T. 2005. Welcome to the revolution: Integrative biology and assessing the impact of endocrine disruptors on environmental and public health. Integrative Comparative Biology 45: 321-329.

Hayes TB, Collins A, Lee M, Mendoza MT, Noriega N, Stuart AA, et al. 2002. Hermaphroditic, demasculinized frogs after exposure to the herbicide atrazine at low ecologically relevant doses. Proc Nat'l Acad Sci 99(8): 5476-5480.

Hayes TB, Khoury v, Narayan A, Nazir M, Park A, Brown T, et al. 2010. Atrazine induces complete feminization and chemical castration in male African clawed frogs (Xenopus laevis). Proc Nat'l Acad Sci 107(10): 4612-4617.

Hecker M, Giesy JP, Jones PD, Jooste AM, Carr JA, Solomon KR, et al. 2004. Plasma sex steroid concentrations and gonadal aromatase activities in African clawed frogs (Xenopous laevis) from South Africa. Environmental Toxicology and Chemistry 23(8): 1996-2007.

Hecker M, Kim WJ, Park J-W, Murphy MB, Villeneuve D, Coady KK, et al. 2005. Plasma concentrations of estradiol and testosterone, gonadal aromatase activity and ultrastructure of the testis in Xenopus laevis exposed to estradiol or atrazine. Aquatic Toxicology 72(4): 383-396.

Hendry WJI, DeBrot BL, Zheng X, Branham WS, Sheehan DM. 1999. Differential activity of diethylstilbestrol versus estradiol as neonatal endocrine disruptors in the female hamster (Mesocricetus auratus) reproductive tract. Biology of Reproduction 61: 91-100.

Hendry WJI, Branham WS, Sheehan DM. 2004. Diethylstilbestrol versus estradiol as neonatal disrupters of the hamster (Mesocricetus auratus) cervix. Biology of Reproduction 70: 1306-1316.

Hodgson E, Levi PE. 1998. Interactions of piperonyl butoxide with cytochrome P450. Piperonyl Butoxide, The Insecticide Synergist, Jones, DG (Ed) Academic Press, New York: pp. 41-53.

Hoyt SC, Westigard PH, Burts EC. 1978. Effects of two synthetic pyrethroids on the codling moth, pear psylla, and various mite species in Northwest apple and pear orchards. J Econ Enotomol 71(3): 431-434.

Hrudey SE, Payment P, Huck PM, Gillham RW, Hrudey EJ. 2003. A fatal waterborne disease epidemic in Walkerton, Ontario: Comparison with other waterborne outbreaks in the developed world. Water Science and Technology 47(3): 7-14.

Hughner RS, McDonagh P, Prothero A, Shultz II CJ, Stanton J. 2007. Who are organic food consumers? A compilation and review of why people purchase organic food. Journal of Consumer Behavior 6: 1-17.

Hull LA, Beers EH, Meagher RL, Jr. 1985. Impact of selective use of the synthetic pyrethroid fenvalerate on apple pests and natural enemies in large-orchard trials. J Econ Enotomol 78: 163-168.

James, L. 2005. Backbreaking work props up 'sustainable' crops. High Country Times, May 2, 2005, vol. 37 (8). Available from:: http://www.hcn.org/servlets/hcn.Article?article_id=15471

Jameson RR, Seidler FJ, Qiao D, Slotkin TA. 2006. Chlorpyrifos affects phenotypic outcomes in a model of mammalian neurodevelopment: Critical stages targeting differentiation in PC12 cells. Environ Health Persp 114(5): 667-672.

Johnson, D. A.; Cummings, T. F.; Rowe, R. C.; Miller, J. S.; Thornton, R. E.; Pelter, G. Q.; Sorensen, E. J. 1997. Potato late blight in the Columbia Basin: An economic analysis of the 1995 epidemic. Plant Disease 81:103-106.

Jones MN. 1999. Surfactants in membrane solubilisation. International Journal of Pharmaceutics 177(2): 137-159.

Katsuda Y. 1999. Development of and future prospects for pyrethroid chemistry. Pesticide Sci 55: 775-782.

Kerby JL, Richards-Hrdlicka KL, Storfer A, Skelly DK. 2010. An examination of amphibian sensitivity to environmental contaminants: are amphibians poor canaries? Ecology Letters 13: 60-67.

Kloas W, Lutz I, Springer T, Krueger HR, Wolf J, Holden L, et al. 2009. Does atrazine influence larval development and sexual differentiation in Xenopus laevis. Toxicological Sciences 107(2): 376-384.

Knutson, R. D.; Hall, C. R.; Smith, E. G.; Cotner, S. D.; Miller, J. W. Economic Impacts of Reduced Pesticide Use on Fruits and Vegetables. American Farm Bureau Research Foundation: Washington, DC, 1993.

Kolpin DW, Goolsby DA, Thurman EM. 1995. Pesticides in near-surface aquifers: an assessment using highly sensitive analytical methods and tritium. J Environ Qual 24(6): 1125-1132.

Kraus N, T.Malmfors, P. Slovic. 1992. Intuitive toxicology: Expert and lay judgements of chemical risks. Risk Analysis 12(2): 215-233.

LaDeau SL, Kilpatrick AM, Marra PP. 2007. West Nile virus emergence and large-scale declines of North American bird populations. Nature 447: 710-714.

Laflamme DM, VanDerslice JA. 2004. Using the behavioral risk factor surveillance system (BRFSS) for exposure tracking: Experiences from Washington State. Environ Health Perspect 112: 1428-1433.

Levine AS, Fellers CR. 1940. Inhibiting effect of acetic acid upon microorganisms in the presence of sodium chloride and sucrose. Journal of Bacteriology 40(2): 255-269.

Long RF, Meyer RD, Orloff SB. 2005. Producing alfalfa hay organically. Proceedings, California Alfalfa and Forage Symposium, 12-14 December, 2005, Visalia, CA, UC Cooperative Extension, Agronomy Research and Extension Center, Plant Sciences Department, University of California, Davis, 95616.

Lynn R, Pagliari C. 1994. The intelligence of American children is still rising. J Biosocial Science 26(1): 65-67.

Mac Kenzie WR, Hoxie NJ, Proctor ME, Gradus MS, Blair KA, Peterson DE, et al. 1994. A massive outbreak in Milwaukee of Cryptosporidium infection transmitted through the public water supply. New England Journal of Medicine 331(3): 161-167.

MacDonald WL. 1995. Pyrethrum flowers —production in Australia. Pyrethrum Flowers Production, Chemistry, Toxicology, and Uses. Casida, J E and Quistad, G B (Eds) Oxford University Press, New York. pp 55-66.

Magnusson MK, Arvola A, Hursti U-KK, Aberg L, Sjopdemn P. 2003. Choice of organic foods is related to perceived consequences for human health and to environmentally friendly behaviour. Appetite 40: 109-117.

Makatouni A. 2002. What motivates consumers to buy organic food in the UK? Results from a qualitative study. British Food Journal 104: 345-352.

Marasas WFO. 2001. Discovery and occurrence of the fumonisins: A historical perspective. Environmental Health Perspectives 109 (Suppl 2): 239-243.

Marc J, Mulner-Lorillon O, Boulben S, Hureau D, Durand G, Belle R. 2002. Pesticide Roundup provokes cell division dysfunction at the level of CDK1/cyclin B activation. Chem Res Toxicol 15: 326-331.

Marty MS, Domoradzki JY, Hansen SC, Timchalk C, Bartels MJ, Mattsson JL. 2007. The effect of route, vehicle, and divided doses on the pharmacokinetics of chlorpyrifos and its metablite trichloropyridinol in neonatal Sprague-Dawley rats. Toxicological Sciences 100(2): 360-373.

McCoy KA, Bortnick LJ, Campbell CM, Hamlin HJ, Guillette LJ, Jr., St. Mary CM. 2008. Agriculture alters gonadal form and function in the toad Bufo marinus. Environ Health Perspect 116: 1526-1532.

McDaniel TV, Martin PA, Struger J, Sherry J, Marvin CH, McMaster ME, et al. 2008. Potential endocrine disruption of sexual development in free ranging male northern leopard frogs (Rana pipiens) and green frogs (Rana clamitans) from areas of intensive row crop agriculture. Aquatic Toxicology 88(4): 230-242.

Melnick R, Lucier G, Wolfe MJ, Hall RE, Stancel GM, Prins G, et al. 2002. Summary of the National Toxicology Program's Report of the Endocrine Disruptors Low-Dose Peer Review. Environ Health Perspect 110: 427-431.

Menn JJ. 1980. Contemporary frontiers in chemical pesticide research. J Agric and Food Chem 28: 2-8.

Menn JJ, Henrick CA. 1981. Rational and biorational design of pesticides. Phil Trans Royal Soc London Seri B, Biological Sciences 295(1076): 55-71

Mertz CK, Slovic P, Purchase IFH. 1998. Judgments of chemical risks: Comparisons among senior managers, toxicologists, and the public. Risk Analysis 18(4): 391-404.

Metcalf, R. L.; Luckmann, W. H. (Eds.) 1975. Introduction to Insect Pest Management. John Wiley & Sons; NY; pp 3-35.

Meyer A, Seidler FJ, Aldridge JE, Tate CA, Cousins MM, Slotkin TA. 2004. Critical periods for chlorpyrifos-induced developmental neurotoxicity: Alterations in adenylyl cyclase signaling in adult rat brain regions after gestational or neonatal exposure. Environmental Health Perspectives 112(3): 295-301.

Mileson BE, Chambers J, Chen WL, Detttbarn W, Ehrich M, Eldefrawi At, et al. 1998. Common mechanism of toxicity: a case study of organophosphorus pesticides. Toxicological Sciences 41(1): 8-20.

Miyamoto J, Kaneko H, Tsuji R, Okuno Y. 1995. Pyrethroids, nerve poisons: how their risks to human health should be assessed. Toxicology Letters 82-83: 933-940.

Morgan MK, Sheldon Ls, Croghan CW, Jones PA, Robertson GL, Chuang JC, et al. 2005. Exposures of preschool children to chlorpyrifos and its degradation product 3,5,6-trichloro-2-pyridinol in their everyday environments. Journal of Exposure Analysis and Environmental Epidemiology 15: 297-309.

Moss GP. 1996. Basic terminology of stereochemistry. Pure & Appl Chem 68: 2193-2222.

Murphy MB, Hecker M, Coady KK, Tompsett AR, Higley EB, Jones PD, et al. 2006. Plasma steroid hormone concentrations, aromatase activities and GSI in ranid frogs collected from agricultural and non-agricultural sites in Michigan (USA). Aquatic Toxicology 77: 153-166.

Narahashi T, Zhao X, Ikeda T, Nagata K, Yeh JZ. 2007. Differential actions of insecticides on target sites: basis for selective toxicity. Human & Experimental Toxicology 26: 361-366.

Narahashi T. 1987. Nerve membrane ion channels as the target sites of environmental toxicants. Environmental Health Perspectives 71: 25-29.

Naranjo SE, Ellsworth PC. 2009. Fifty years of the integrated control concept: moving the model and implementation forward in Arizona. Pest Management Science 65: 1267-1286.

National Research Council. The Future Role of Pesticides in U.S. Agriculture; National Academy Press: Washington, DC, 2000; pp. 17-32.

Newschaffer CJ, Croen LA, Daniels J, Giarelli E, Grether JK, Levy SE, et al. 2007. The epidemiology of autism spectrum disorders. Ann Rev Public Health 28: 235-258.

Newton M, Howard KM, Kelpsas BR, Danhaus R, Lottman CM, Dubelman. S. 1984. Fate of glyphosate in an Oregon forest ecosystem. J Agric Food Chem 32: 1144-1151.

Oka T, Tooi O, Mitsui N, Miyahara M, Ohnishi Y, Takase M, et al. 2008. Effect of atrazine on metamorphosis and sexual differentiation in Xenopus laevis. Aquatic Toxicology 87: 215-226.

Orr N, Shaffner AJ, Richey K, Crouse GD. 2009. Novel mode of action of spinosad: Receptor binding studies demonstrating lack of interaction with known insecticidal target sites. Pesticide Biochem Physiol 95: 1-5.

Padgitt, M.; Newton, D.; Penn, R.; Sandretto, C. L. 2000. Production Practices in U.S. Agriclture, 1990-97, Statistical Bulletin. U.S. Department of Agriculture, Economic Research Service, Washington, DC. Available from: http://www.ers.usda.gov/publications/sb969/sb969.pdf

Pathan IB, Setty CM. 2009. Chemical penetration enhancers for transdermal drug delivery systems. Tropical Journal of Pharmaceutical Research 8(2): 173-179.

Payne-Sturges D, Cohen J, Castorina R, Axelrad DA, Woodruff TJ. 2009. Evaluating cumulative organophosphorus pesticide body burden of children: A national case study. Environ Sci and Technol 43: 7924-7930.

Pell MB, Morris J. 2008. Perils of the new pesticides. Center for Public Integrity. Available from: http://www.publicintegrity.org/investigations/pesticides/pages/introduction/.

Peterson RKD, Macedo PA, Davis RS. 2006. A human-health risk assessment for West Nile virus and insecticides used in mosquito management. Environmental Health Perspectives 114: 366-372.

Pimentel, D.; Acquay, H.; Biltonen, M.; Rice, P.; Silva, M.; Nelson, J.; Lipner, V.; Giorgano, S.; Horowitz, A.; D'Amore, M. 1992. Environmental and economic costs of pesticide use. Bioscience 42(10): 750-760.

Pimentel D, Harvey C, Resosudarmo P, Sinclair K, Kurz D, McNair M, et al. 1995. Environmental and economic costs of soil erosion and conservation benefits. Science 267: 1117-1123.

Pluijmen M, Drevon C, Montesano R, Malaveille C, Hautefeuille A, Bartsch H. 1984. Lack of mutagenicity of synthetic pyrethroids in Salmonella typhimurium strains and in V79 Chinese hamster cells. Mutation Research/Genetic Toxicology 137(1): 7-15.

Okulicz WC, Leavitt WW. 1988. Binding and biologic activity of diethylsilbestrol in the hamster: Influence of a serum component on estrogen receptor binding and estrogenic activity. Journal of Steroid Biochemistry 31(4): 371-375.

Qiao D, Seidler FJ, Tate CA, Cousins MM, Slotkin TA. 2003. Fetal chlorpyrifos exposure: Adverse effects on brain cell development and cholinergic biomarkers emerge postnatally and continue into adolescence and adulthood. Environ Health Persp 111(4): 536-544.

Qiao D. 2010. Development of health criteria for school site risk assessment persuant to health and safety code section 901(g): Child-specific reference dose (chRD) for school site risk assessment-chlorpyrifos. Final Report, June 2010, Integrated Risk Assessment Branch, Office of Environmental Health Hazard Assessment, California Environmental Protection Agency.

Qin S, Liu W, Gan J. 2008. Chiral selectivity in the environmental fate of pyrethroids. Synthetic Pyrethroids, ACS Symposium Series 991:238-253.

Ramesh A, Ravi PE. 2004. Electron ionization gas chromatography-mass spectrometric determination of residues of thirteen pyrethoid insecticides in whole blood. Journal of Chromatography B 802: 371-376.

Raven G, de Jong FH, Kaufman J-M, de Ronde W. 2006. In men, peripheral estradiol levels directly reflect the action of estrogens at they hypothalamo-pituitary level to inhibit gonadotropin secretion. Journal of Clinical Endocrinology & Metabolism 91: 3324-3328.

Ray DE, Forshaw PJ. 2000. Pyrethoird insecticides: Poisoning syndromes, synergies, and therapy. Clinical Toxicology 38(2): 95-101.

Reganold JP, Andrews PK, Reeve Jr, CarpenterBoggs L, Schadt CW, Alldredge Jr, et al. 2010. Fruit and soil quality of organic and conventional strawberry agroecosystems. PLOS One 5(9): e12346.

Relyea RA. 2005a. Pesticides and amphibians: The importance of community context. Ecological Applications 15(4): 1125-1134.

Relyea RA. 2005b. The impact of insecticides and herbicides on the biodiversity and productivity of aquatic communities. Ecological Applications 15(2): 618-627.

Relyea RA. 2005c. The lethal impacts of Roundup and predatory stress on six species of North American tadpoles. Arch Environ Contam Toxicol 48: 351-357.

Relyea RA. 2005d. The lethal impact of Roundup on aquatic and terrestrial amphibians. Ecological Applications 15(4): 1118-1124.

Richard J, Junk GA, Avery MJ, Nehring NL, Fritz JS, Svec HJ. 1975. Analysis of various Iowa waters for selected pesticides: atrazine, DDE, and dieldrin—1974. Pesticides Monitoring J 9:117-123.

Richard S, Moslemi S, Sipahutar H, Benachour N, Seralini G-E. 2005. Differential effects of glyphosate and Roundup on human placental cells and aromatase. Environmental Health Perspectives 113: 716-720.

Richards RP, Baker BR, Christensen BR, Tierney DP. 1995. Atrazine exposures through drinking water: exposure assessments for Ohio, Illinois, and Iowa. Environmental Science & Technology 29(2): 406-412.

Roberts DR, Laughlin LL, Hsheih P, Legters LJ. 1997. DDT, global strategies, and a malaria control crisis in South America. Emerging Infectious Diseases 3(3): 295-302.

Robertson GP, Paul EA, Harwood RR. 2000. Greenhouse gases in intensive agriculture: Contributions of individual gases to the radiative forcing of the atmosphere. Science 289: 1922-1925.

Rondon, S. I.; Gray, M. E. 2004. Ovarian development and ovipositional preferences of the western corn rootworm (Coleoptera: Chrysomelidae) variant in east central Illinois. J. Econ. Entomol. 97:390-396.

Rusiecki JA, De Roos AJ, Lee WJ, Dosemeci M, Lubin JH, Hoppin JA, et al. 2004. Cancer incidence among pesticide applicators exposed to atrazine in the Agricultural Health Study. J National Cancer Institute 96(18): 1375-1382.

Saba A, Messina F. 2003. Attitudes towards organic foods and risk/benefit perception associated with pesticides. Food Quality and Preference 14: 637-645.

Sammons, A. E.; Edwards, C. R.; Bledsoe, L. W.; Boeve, P. J.; Stuart, J. J. Environ. Entomol. 1997, 26, 1336-1342.

Scribner EA, Battaglin WA, Gilliom RJ, Meyer MT. 2007. Concentrations of glyphosate, its degradation product, aminomethylphosphonic acid, and glufosinate in ground- and surface-water, rainfall, and soil samples collected in the United States, 2001-06. US Geological Survey Scientific Investigations Report 2007-5122: 111 pp.

Schonbrunn E, Eschenburg S, Shuttleworth WA, Schloss JV, Amrhein N, Evans JNS, et al. 2001. Interaction of the herbicide glyphosate with its target enzyme 5-enolpyruvylshikimate 3-phosphate synthase in atomic detail. Proceedings of the National Academy of Sciences 98(4): 1376-1380.

Sikorski JA, Gruys KJ. 1997. Understanding glyphosate's molecular mode of action with EPSP synthase:, evidence favoring an allosteric inhibitor model. Accounts of Chemical Research 30(1): 2-8

Slovic P. 1987. Perception of risk. Science 236: 280-285.

Slovic P. 1999. Trust, emotion, sex, politics, and science: Surveying the risk-assessment battlefield. Risk Analysis 19: 689-701.

Slotkin TA, Levin ED, Seidler FJ. 2006. Comparative developmental neurotoxicity of organophosphate insecticides: Effects on brain development are separable from systemic toxicity. Environ Health Persp 114(5): 746-751.

Slotkin TA, Seidler FJ, Fumagalli F. 2010. Unrelated developmental neurotoxicants elicit similar transcriptional profiles for effects on neurotrophic factors and their receptors in an in vitro model. Neurotoxicology and Teratology 32: 2010.

Slotkin TA. 1999. Developmental Cholinotoxicants: Nicotine and Chlorpyrifos. Environmental Health Perspectives 107(Supplement 1): 71-80.

Smith EE, Du Preez L, Gentles A, Solomon KR, Tandler B, Carr JA, et al. 2005. Assessment of laryngeal muscle and testicular cell types in Xenopus laevis (Anura Pipidae) inhabiting maize and non-maize growing areas of South Africa. African Journal of Herpetology 54(1): 69-76.

Soderlund DM, Bloomquist JR. 1989. Neurotoxic actions of pyrethroid insecticides. Ann Rev Entomol 34: 77-96.

Solomon KR, Anadón A, Carrasquilla G, Cerdeira AL, Marshall J, Sanin LH. 2007. Coca and poppy eradication in Colombia: Environmental and human health assessment of aerially applied glyphosate. Rev Environ Contam Toxicol 190: 43-125.

Solomon KR, Baker Db, Richards RP, Dixon Kr, Klaine SJ, LaPoint TW, et al. 1996. Ecological risk assessment of atrazine in North American surface waters. Environ Toxicol Chem 15(1): 31-76.

Solomon KR, Thompson DG. 2003. Ecological risk assessment for aquatic organism from over-water uses of glyphosate. Journal of Toxicology and Environmental Health, Part B 6: 289-324.

Song X, Seidler FJ, Saleh JL, Zhang J, Padilla S, Slotkin TA. 1997. Cellular mechanisms for developmental toxicity of chlorpyrifos: targeting the adenylyl cyclase signaling cascade. Toxicology and Applied Pharmacology 145(1): 158-174.

Sparks TC, Crouse GD, Durst G. 2001. Natural products as insecticides: the biology, biochemistry and quantitative structure–activity relationships of spinosyns and spinosoids. Pest Management Science 57: 896-905.

Spolyarich N, Hyne R, Wilson SC, Palmer C, Byrne M. 2010. Growth, development and sex ratios of Spotted Marsh Frog (Limnodynastes tasmaniensis) larvae exposed to atrazine and an herbicide mixture. Chemosphere 78: 807-813.

Steenland K, Dick RB, Howell RJ, Chrislip DW, Hines CJ, Reid TM, et al. 2000. Neurologic function among termiticide applicators exposed to chlorpyrifos. Environ Health Perspect 108: 293-300.

Stern VM, Smith RF, van den Bosch R, Hagen KS. 1959. The integrated control concept. Hilgardia 29: 81-101.

Stevens JT, Tobia A, Lamb JCI, Tellone C, O'Neal F. 1997. FIFRA Subdivision F Testing Guidelines: Are these tests adequate to detect potential hormonal activity for crop protection chemicals? J Environ Toxicol Environ Health, Part A 50(5): 415-431.

Sullivan, D.J., Vecchia, A.V., Lorenz, D.L., Gilliom, R.J., and Martin, J.D., 2009, Trends in pesticide concentrations in corn-belt streams, 1996–2006: U.S. Geological Survey Scientific Investigations Report 2009–5132, 75 p.

Suomalainen TH, Mayra-Makinen AM. 1999. Propionic acid bacteria as protective cultures in fermented milks and breads. Lait 79: 165-174.

Szpir M. 2006. Tracing the origins of autism. A spectrum of new studies. Environ Health Persp 114(A412-A418).

Taylor, C. R. Economic Impacts and Environmental and Food Safety Tradeoffs of Pesticide Use Reduction on Fruit and Vegetables. Dept. Agricultural Economics and Rural Sociology, Auburn University: Auburn, AL, 1995.

Teasdale TW, Owen DR. 2008. Secular declines in cognitive test scores: A reversal of the Flynn effect. Intelligence 36: 121-126.

Thompson DG, Wojtaszek BF, Staznik B, Chartrand T, Stephenson GR. 2004. Chemical and biomonitoring to assess potential acute effects of Vision herbicide on native amphibian larvae in forest wetlands. Environmental Toxicology and Chemistry 23(4): 843-849.

Tickner J. 2002. Guest editorial. Public Health Reports 117: 493-497.

Timchalk C, Nolan RJ, Mendrala AL, Dittenber DA, Brzak KA, Mattsson JL. 2002. A physiologically based pharmacokinetic and pharmacodynamic (PBPK/PD) model for the organophosphate insecticide chlorpyrifos in rats and humans. Toxicological Sciences 66: 34-53.

Tsui MTK, Chu LM. 2008. Environmental fate and non-target impact of glyphosate-based herbicide (Roundup) in a subtropical wetland. Chemosphere 71: 439-446.

USDA AMS (Agricultural Marketing Service). 2009. Pesticide Data Program—Annual Summary, Calendar 2008. Available from: http://www.ams.usda.gov/AMSv1.0/pdp

USDA Historical Track Records, April 2005, Available from: http://usda.mannlib.cornell.edu/reports/nassr/field/pcp-bb/2005/croptr05.pdf

USDA National Agricultural Statistics Service (NASS). 2009. 2007 Census of Agriculture-United States; Available from: http://www.agcensus.usda.gov/Publications/2007/Full_Report/index.asp

USDA National Agricultural Statistics Service. Agricultural Chemical Usage 2003 Fruit Summary, 2004; Available from: http://usda.mannlib.cornell.edu/MannUsda/viewDocumentInfo.do?documentID=1560

USDA National Agricultural Statistics Service. Agricultural Chemical Usage 2004 Field Crops Summary, 2005; Available from: http://usda.mannlib.cornell.edu/MannUsda/viewDocumentInfo.do?documentID=1560

USDA National Agricultural Statistics Service. Agricultural Chemical Usage 2004 Field Crops Summary, 2007; Available from: http://usda.mannlib.cornell.edu/ MannUsda/viewDocumentInfo.do?documentID=1560

vom Saal FS, Timms BG, Montano MM, Palanza P, Thayer KA, Nagel SC, et al. 1997. Prostate enlargement in mice due to fetal exposure to low doses of estradiol or diethylstilbestrol and opposite effects at high doses. Proc Natl Acad Sci USA 94: 2056-2061.

Wainaina JMG. 1995. Pyrethrum flowers—production in Africa. Pyrethrum Flowers Production, Chemistry, Toxicology, and Uses. Casida, J E and Quistad, G B (Eds) Oxford University Press, New York. pp 49-54.

Wang N, Besser JM, Buckler DR, Honegger JL, Ingersoll CG, Johnson BT, et al. 2005. Influence of seimdent on the fate and toxicity of a polyethoxylated tallowamine surfactant system (MON 0818) in aquatic microcosms. Chemosphere 59: 545-551.

Weston DP, Holmes RW, You J, Lydy MJ. 2005. Aquatic toxicity due to residential use of pyrethroid insecticides. Environ Sci Technol 39: 9778-9784.

Whitney KK, Seidler FJ, Slotkin TA. 1995. Developmental neurotoxicity of chlorpyrifos: cellular mechanisms. Toxicol Appl Pharmacol 134: 53-62

Williams GM, Kroes R, Munro IC. 2000. Safety evaluation and risk assessment of the herbicide Rounup and its acitve ingredient, glyphosate, for humans. Regulatory Toxicology and Pharmacology 31: 117-165.

Wilson NK, Strauss WJ, Iroz-Elardo N, Chuang JC. 2010. Exposures of preschool children to chlorpyrifos, diazinon, pentachlorophenol, and 2,4-dichlorophenoxyacetic acid over 3 years from 2003 to 2005: A longitudinal model. Journal of Exposure Science and Environmental Epidemiology 20: 546-558.

Wojtaszek BF, Staznik B, Chartrand DT, Stephenson GR, Thompson DG. 2004. Effects of Vision herbicide on mortality, avoidance response, and growth of amphibian larvae in two forest wetlands. Environ Toxicol Chem 23(4): 832-842.

World Health Organization (WHO). 2005. Glyphosate and AMPA in drinking-water. WHO/SDE/WSH/0304/97: Available from: http://www.who.int/ water_sanitation_health/.

World Health Organization (WHO). 2010. Atrazine and its metabolites in drinking-water Background document for development of WHO Gidelines for Drinking-water Quality. Available from: http://www.who.int/water_sanitation_health/dwq/chemicals/atrazine/en/index.html.

World Health Organization (WHO). 2010. Malaria, Fact Sheet No. 94. Available from: http://www.who.int/mediacentre/factsheets/fs094/en/

Wu F. 2006. Mycotoxin reduction in Bt corn: Potential economic, health, and regulatory impacts. Transgenic Research 15: 277-289.

WSDA (Washington State Department of Agriculture). 2010. WSDA Approved Input List. Washington State Department of Agriculture Organic Program.

Yang D, Howard A, Bruun D, Ajua-Alemanj M, Pickart C, Lein PJ. 2008. Chlorpyrifos and chlorpyrifos-oxon inhibit axonal growth by interfering with the morphogenic activity of acetylcholinesterase. Toxicol Appl Pharmacol 228(1): 32-41.

You J, Pehkonen SO, Weston DP, Lydy MJ. 2008. Chemical availability and sediment toxicity of pyrethroid insecticides to Hyalella azteca: Application to field sediment with unexpectedly low toxicity. Environmental Toxicology and Chemistry 27(10): 2124-2130.

Yiridoe EK, Bonti-Ankomah S, Martin RC. 2005. Comparison of consumer perceptions and preference toward organic versus conventionally produced foods: A review and update of the literature. Renewable Agriculture and Food systems 20(4): 193-205.

Zehnder G, Gurr GM, Kuhne S, Wade MR, Wratten SD, Wyss Ed. 2007. Arthropod pest management in organic crops. Ann Rev Entomol 52: 57-80.

Zhang XC, Driver JH, Li Y, Rposs JH, Krieger RI. 2008. Dialkylphosphates (DAPs) in fruits and vegetables may confound biomonitoring in organophosphrus insecticide exposure and risk assessment. J Agric Food Chem 56: 10638-10645

Zilberman D, Schmitz A, Casterline G, Lichtenberg E, Siebert JB, 1991. The economics of pesticide use and regulation. Science 253:518-522.

References

110

The opinions expressed in ACSH publications do not necessarily represent
the views of all members of the ACSH Board of Trustees, Founders Circle and
Board of Scientific and Policy Advisors, who all serve without compensation.

Made in the USA
Middletown, DE
30 April 2018